A U S T R A L I A N

LEGENDS
and LANDSCAPES

AUSTRALIAN

LEGENDS
and LANDSCAPES

OODGEROO NOONUCCAL

with photography by
Reg Morrison

RANDOM HOUSE
AUSTRALIA

ACKNOWLEDGEMENTS

Thanks go to Magabala Books for permission to republish "Laying Down", "Rain", "Galinji" and "Do Not Go Around the Edges (Bunju Bunju)"; to Rigby Publishers for "How the People Were All Drowned"; and to the Mutitjulu Community and Australian National Parks and Wildlife Service for "The Mala Story" and "The Mutitjulu Story".
The particular helpfulness of Peter Bibby, Keith Taylor, Graham Dillon, Jon Willis, Jennifer Isaacs and Brian Prince are much appreciated.

Random House Australia;
an imprint of Random Century Australia Pty Ltd
1st Floor, 20 Alfred Street, Milsons Point,
New South Wales 2061.

Sydney London Auckland Johannesburg
and agencies throughout the world.

Produced for the publisher
by Bow Books.

National Library of Australia
Cataloguing-in-Publication data:

Legends and landscapes.

ISBN 0 09 169820 0.

[1]. Aborigines, Australian — Legends.
I. Noonuccal, Oodgeroo, 1920–   II. Morrison, Reg.

398.2049915

Designed by Karen Jeffery, K.J. Graphics Pty Limited
Typeset by InterType Pty. Ltd.
Printed in Australia

Photo Sources
All photographs are by
Reg Morrison, Auscape International,
unless otherwise indicated.

Noonuccal corroboree dancers, Raymond, Che and Joshua Walker recreate a fragment of their heritage.

*A*ll human legends are many things. They record our history. They inform us of our geographical places, of good and evil. They are our communication with each other. In the Aboriginal instance, each separate tribe has its own unique legends, traditionally passed down through word of mouth from generation to generation.

Originally, there were 350 entirely separate Aboriginal languages and 750 dialects; the tribes of Australia had a rich and diverse culture, as do all grass-roots tribes of the world. The Australian invasion 200 years ago disrupted our way of living, and in some cases completely wiped out many of our tribes and with them were lost forever a lot of the culture. In spite of this attempted genocide, the Australian Aborigines lived on, though badly depleted in numbers and tribes.

The sad history of the invasion, and the brutality that occurred and is still occurring — the brutality is now psychological and subliminal, not physical, and therefore not as blatant as it was — sparked and fuelled the fires burning in the hearts of all the tribes. Every tribe bears the scars of the violence that occurred, even today.

The Aboriginal legends were recorded by many of the invaders, who saw it as a way of making money. Always when the white man recorded the legends, he would milk dry the knowledge from the elders without any thought of the teller of the legends. The Aborigines were blatantly used in this way. After extracting the knowledge from the Aborigine, the white writer would return to the security of his world and hope his book would become a best seller. He cared little or nothing for the tribesmen or women who passed the knowledge on to him. He just walked away and left the narrators sitting dispossessed in the red Australian dust.

Those white researchers and university students who recorded these legends were able to climb higher up their social ladder to acceptance and success in the eyes of their peers. They also became possessive of their recordings, and carefully guarded them. So the theft was completed, and accepted by their peers without any thought of guilt.

Looking south down Main Beach from Point Lookout, Stradbroke Island.

In the Aboriginal world of writing, no one must write about another tribe's legends or way of life without first receiving permission to do so. Also, full credit must be accorded. The uncivilised invaders still have a lot to learn about the good manners practised even today between the Aboriginal tribes. This practice, I believe, is called protocol by the white invaders, but was not practised when dealing with the proud and dignified Aboriginal tribes.

I hope this book will help put the record straight and that the present generation of the white Australian invaders will at long last start listening and learning some of the truths from the orators within the Aboriginal tribes. In this respect, I have found that most of the ethnic groups within and outside Australia are more civilised and better mannered than the seventh-generation Australian.

However, some seventh-generation Australians are now listening and learning from us. Let us hope that this is a habit-forming exercise and more of them will follow suit and start listening and learning, so that finally we can wipe out ignorance from the Australian scene.

Our legends tell of the spirit world and they go back to the Alcheringa (now renamed "Dreamtime" without our permission). We know that the earth is our mother who created us all. We cannot own her, she owns us. So we are the custodians of our Earth Mother, whom we must respect and protect at all times. The damage done to the Australian environment over the last 200 years shows that many of the white strangers who came amongst us did not understand this need for respect and protection.

When Aboriginal children are born, they are given a child name; when they are entering adulthood they are given an adult name, and with it goes full responsibility for their actions. They are named after other living things. For instance my name, Oodgeroo, means "paperbark tree". My responsibility is to protect, wherever and whenever I can, my sisters the paperbark trees.

This is pure conservation and protection of all the Earth Mother's creations. All living things, be they mammals, birds, reptiles, insects or trees are our sisters and brothers and therefore we must protect them. We are their custodians. We not only share with them, we also guard them.

The legends are created around our own lore. The lore of the Aborigine is stronger that the white man's law and has stood the test of time, unlike that of the invaders and their descendants, which is being changed continually.

The legends are told mostly at night around camp fires. Some tell of evil spirits who lie in wait for naughty children. When the children hear the legends they keep close to the camp fires, and do not stray away and get lost. They are taught from a very early age that safety lies in numbers.

Our waterholes are where evil spirits live and the children are taught that should they go to the waterhole alone the evil spirit will capture them forever. Our children never go near lakes, swamps, waterholes or the sea, without their adults.

The legends are told and retold to the children until they can repeat them by heart. The elder children then pass them on to their younger brothers and sisters.

There are legends also about the ways of the mammals, birds, reptiles and insects. About how they got their stripes or spots, or how they came to be able to camouflage themselves by changing their colours.

The legend of our Earth Mother and her travels all over the land is pointed out to the children by the elders, saying, "The Earth Mother slept here and when she created rain, she told the rain to fill the tracks of her wanderings and the rain created the swamps and the lakes and the waterholes." The rocks of our Australian land are the Earth Mother's sentries. They stand guard over her and all her creatures, human or otherwise; we know them as our living temples.

Our sun spirit warms and watches over us by day, and at night he leaves the sky to rest. Moon spirit spends many nights bloating herself to full size and then reducing herself to a faint pencil arc in the sky. The stars are recorded in our legends also.

We are as one with the universe; even our dead are but a hair's breadth away from us. We can and do communicate with our departed, for their spirits roam their own beloved tribal lands. They come and go as freely as they wish.

Our legends are also of the sea and all its creatures. We know if we respect the sea she will respond by giving to us her many foods. When the Noonuccal's sea spirit Quandamooka grows angry, she orders us away from her shores, and we wait until she has exhausted her anger and is calm and serene again, before we venture out on to her waters.

Our legends are our bond between our Earth Mother, the sea, and the sky. Between ourselves and our tribespeople, between the living and the dead, between all living things. We are rich in spite of the stolen lands, in spite of the racists, in spite of being dispossessed, for our legends keep us alive, warm and happy.

May this book enrich the lives of others. May it educate and teach. May it give to its readers an insight into our rich and diverse culture, which we the Aborigines of Australia are prepared to share, as we have always shared with all living creatures.

OODGEROO

of the tribe

NOONUCCAL

custodian of the land

MINJERRIBAH

Brooking Gorge, Oscar Range, South Kimberley.

CONTENTS

A WORD FROM THE PHOTOGRAPHER

For an average Australian city dweller like me it is a very sobering experience to find yourself one day standing naked and utterly alone in the silence of a desert twilight. As familiar shapes and the comforting perspectives of daytime gradually disappear and the immensity of the night sky begins to yawn above you, it is hard to avoid the feeling that humanity's last ten thousand years of cultural evolution are tiptoeing quietly away into the night as you stand there, leaving you face to face with your real self. Face to face with the inescapable truth: when the social and technological armour is stripped away inside there lurks just another animal, and a pretty ordinary one at that. Worse, we are the least specialised and most vulnerable of all mammals: one that lacks fur, claws and fighting teeth. One which, if left to its own devices in that setting, would generally not see out the week.

Bereft of our customary insulation from the environment we become part of it again, just as were our human ancestors throughout their two million years of evolution.

It was certainly so for Australia's original occupants, those adventurous nomadic peoples who first settled the continent, perhaps as much as 110,000 years ago. At the cutting edge of human evolution, those exploratory bands of expert hunter-gatherers had pushed the boundaries of human distribution across the seas and beyond its ancient Afro-Eurasian continental base for the very first time.

The modern Aborigines, descended in part from those first settlers, represent the last outpost of that main evolutionary stream, the final flag-bearers of our original human heritage. Well tuned to environmental coexistence by the dictates of their nomadic way of life, and honed by hardship during the onset of Australia's present aridity, they stood at the pinnacle of a million years of unbroken cultural evolution. They were space-age hunter-gatherers. These were not a people who needed reminding of their kinship with the earth. They knew too well that the land owns us all.

What follows is a collection of Aboriginal stories from around Australia, stories that explain the world from that perspective. While it is not a view you can get from the average city window, it is one that the world, in this time of environmental crisis, would do well to heed.

Reg Morrison

Bonaparte
Archipelago

East Alligator River

Kakadu
National Park

Kimberley
Plateau

Mowanjum

NORTHERN
TERRITORY

QUEENSLAND

WESTERN AUSTRALIA

Uluru

Warburton Range

Gold Coast

Stradbroke
Island

SOUTH AUSTRALIA

Mount Warning

Darling Range

NEW SOUTH WALES

Swan River

VICTORIA

Furneaux
Group

Lake Saint Clair

Mount Ben Lomond

TASMANIA

AUSTRALIA

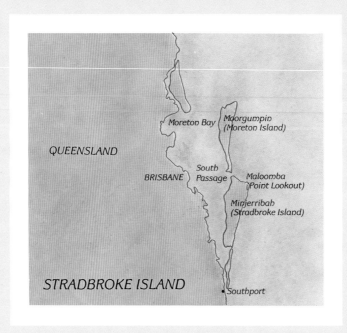

STRADBROKE ISLAND

Noonuccal is the name of the Aboriginal people of Minjerribah (Stradbroke Island).
The Noonuccal's totem and custodian is Kabul, carpet snake; she represents the Rainbow Serpent who sleeps at Uluru.

These stories are told by Oodgeroo, custodian of Minjerribah.

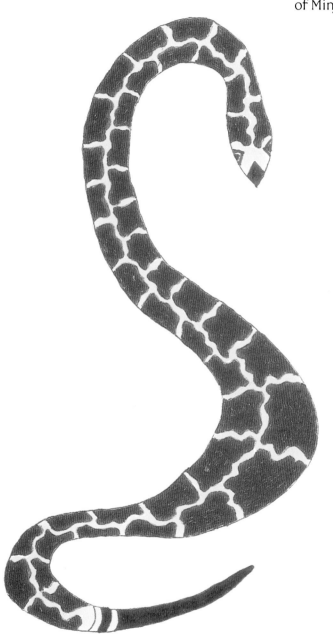

Kabul, the carpet snake, is the Noonuccal totem. She is pictured here with many Noonuccal babies in her belly waiting to be born. Drawing by Oodgeroo Noonuccal.

15

The widening gap between Stadbroke and Moreton Islands
is part of a process that began more than 10,000 years
ago when rising sea levels began to eat into coastlines
all around Australia. Related clans on each island who
could once walk to visit each other soon had to take
canoes. These coast she-oaks are the latest victims of the
invading sea.

MERRIPOOL — CALLER OF THE WINDS

Large baler shells like this one held great significance for the island peoples of Moreton and Stradbroke. They represented the spiritual birthplace of the winds that so modulated tribal life in that region. As such, the shells were also considered fitting markers for traditional burial sites.

Merripool was a member of the Noonuccal Tribe of Minjerribah (Stradbroke Island). He was the custodian or keeper of the four winds. He carried the secret of the winds around in a bailer shell.

The Nughies of Moorgumpin (Moreton Island) became jealous of Merripool's power and they met one day to set up a plan to ambush Merripool and steal from him his bailer. During this time Moreton and Stradbroke Islands were joined together.

When Merripool found out about the plan to ambush and trick him, he became very angry. He took his bailer shell away with him even from his own tribe the Noonuccal. He set the bailer shell down on the sand and called the four winds to come to him.

When the four winds came he talked to them, "If this is the wrong thing for the Nughies to do I ask you four winds North, South, East, West to come

Vine-covered mangrove trees
on Stradbroke Island.

Right
Flinders Beach, Stradbroke Island.

to my call and do something about it." He went to the hill top and he called, and he called, and he called to the winds.

He called for many days and nights and his voice came louder and louder. He called for so long even his own tribe the Noonuccal became frightened and begged him to stop.

But Merripool kept on calling and the winds blew for many days and many nights and they blew so hard, that they caused the water to cut Moorgumpin away from Minjerribah. The passage between the two islands is now called the South Passage and it is the entrance into the Port of Brisbane.

The Nughies were stranded on Moorgumpin and when the animals and reptiles saw the break coming, they joined the Noonuccals on Minjerribah, and the Nughies were dependent on Quandamooka the sea spirit for their food. After the winds died down Merripool called his people together and told them it would be their duty to feed the Nughies and give them shelter, but because of their treachery the Nughies could never again be trusted.

18

When all four winds are safely confined in the great baler shell of Merripool, the people of Stradbroke Island may still enjoy moments such as these at Beimea (Brown Lake). The words *karboora* (brown) and *beimea* (blue) were mistakenly transposed by white settlers; Brown Lake should really be known as Karboora.

Following page
Dawn breaks at North Gorge, Stradbroke Island.

LEGEND OF MOOLOOMBA (POINT LOOKOUT)

The legend of Mooloomba and the creation of Wailing Rock is the modern tip of an iceberg of tribal memory that outspans the whole of Western civilisation. Like both of the other Stradbroke Island stories it tells of encroaching seas. In this it represents an oral tradition that would have begun some 10,000 years ago as the last glacial era began to relax its grip on the world and the sea became charged with meltwater from the huge polar icecaps. Vast areas of coastal Australia became inundated, reducing the Moreton-Stradbroke region first to a peninsula and finally to an island chain. Such territorial losses would have had a major impact on tribal life and consequently on the oral culture of the region.

*B*efore the whites came, the Noonuccal Tribe roamed freely over their island territory, going on walkabouts, continualiy on the move, searching for food.

One day they decided to go to the northernmost part of the island, which they called Minjerribah.

Now there was an old woman of the tribe who was always complaining. This day she was nagging the tribe about food, that she never got enough or it was poor quality and that the tribe treated her badly all the time. The tribal elders got very angry with her and told her to stop complaining, but she would not.

The vast sweep of sand that now forms Stradbroke Island's
Outside Beach was piled there by the icy winds of the last
glacial era, when the seas receded to expose the full width
of the Australian continental shelf. As the coastline
migrated eastward this area became part of a well-
watered coastal plain and would have provided an inland
summer food-gathering ground for the ancestors of the
Noonuccal Tribe. It is likely that Aboriginal occupation of
this food-rich region occurred early, at least 20,000 years
ago and perhaps much more.

Following Pages
The pandanus palm was a useful resource for the people
of Moreton and Stradbroke. It provided them with a little
food in its fruits, brushes from its fibrous roots and, when
it was burnt, black pigment for painting in its charcoal.
Meanwhile its strong foothold in loose sand helped to
stabilise the shorelines of their wind-lashed island home.
These stand near Point Lookout.

Finally, the elders ordered her to be tied to a stake in the ground at the far end of the island. "Stay there and growl to yourself," they told her. "When we return with the food we will share it with you." They left her still growling and went inland of the island.

Suddenly a huge storm arose from the sea and the Noonuccal Tribe had to shelter as best they could. The storm lasted a long time and ice fell from the sky and the lightning flashed and the thunder roared.

When finally the storm moved away from the island, they gathered their hunting tools and food and went as fast as they could back to the end of the island, worrying about the old woman they had tied to the stake.

When they arrived they were horrified to find the end of the island rock, where they had tied the old woman, had been cut away from the island by the electrical storm. They tried to reach her, but the winds were still howling and they could not. They tried throwing food to her but it fell down into the raging sea. The old woman was crying for them to help her, but there was nothing they could do to get to her. The winds howled for many days and many nights and finally the old woman died.

Now when the winds blow all the Noonuccal Tribe can hear her death cries and the sea sends a spout of water high in the air to remind the Noonuccals of this terrible thing they did. All Noonuccals know that the punishment will always be with them, they will always hear her death cries and the sea will always send a huge spray of water high into the air to remind them. The punishment will pass to their children and their children's children and their children's children's children for as long as the Noonuccal Tribe lives.

NOTE: There is a blowhole at the end of Minjerribah at Mooloomba (Point Lookout).

LEGEND OF THE NOONUCCAL AND NOOGHIE TRIBES

Raymond, Che and Joshua Walker dance on Stradbroke Island.

Left
Fire-blackened scars like this on a small number of old gum trees are among the few visual reminders that remain of the island's original inhabitants. The scar marks the place where bark was stripped to make a canoe for fishing and inter-island travel. The ends of the canoes were usually sealed with beeswax and a fire was sometimes carried aboard on a bed of sand or seaweed, so that fish could be cooked and eaten immediately.

Mutallo the old one, who had twice seen the fire in the sky (Halley's comet), could not remember when the Nughies of Moorgumpin (Moreton Island) first called to the Noonuccal Tribe of Minjerribah (Stradbroke Island), that they would come and chase them into the hills. But the Noonuccal Tribe was strong and feared no one. Every day the Nughies would call across the passage of water (South Passage) separating the two islands.

Then one day Compulla, the fish caller of the Noonuccals, awoke and found a strange and lasting sickness (smallpox) which killed many of the Noonuccal Tribe. The Nughies, hearing no call back from the Noonuccal Tribe, sent Panderook the strong one to see why the Noonuccals were not answering their calls.

In the light of a half moon Panderook saw the once great tribe of the Noonuccals lying scattered around Campulla and their camp fires. He returned to Moorgumpin and told the Nughie Tribe what he had seen.

The Nughies boarded their canoes and quickly crossed the narrow waters of the South Passage. As they came upon the Noonuccal Tribe they cried out to them, "We have come to chase you back into the hills."

From one of the Noonuccals' fires Wanderoo the fire maker rose and facing the Nughies he called, "My people have lived here since the Dreamtime, and you are the first to come without peace in your hearts, to you and to all others this island will never belong. For every sun-up and every sunset you will watch this island disappear into the sea until only the rocky hill stones of Mooloomba (Point Lookout) remain."

NOTE: The land at Amity Point has been slowly swallowed up by Quandamooka (Moreton Bay), the Noonuccals' sea spirit.

Right

According to Aboriginal totemic belief each member of the clan automatically inherited at birth a totemic relationship with a particular plant or animal of the region. They thereby became responsible for the general welfare of that species. The word Oodgeroo, for example, means paperbark tree. The bearer of the totem would count these elegant saplings as part of their family. While individual plants or animals might be used to serve tribal needs, a decline of the species reflected badly on its human relatives. It was this deep, familial interdependence, universally practised throughout Aboriginal Australia, that held the key to their remarkably low impact on regional ecologies that were, in some cases, exceptionally fragile.

GOLD COAST HINTERLAND

Burleigh Head, like the other basalt headlands
that interrupt the broad sweep of Gold Coast
beaches, is a small scrap of Wollumbin (Mount
Warning) lava that has survived 20 million years of
erosion. To the local tribes however, it represents, in
tangible form, the spirit of Jabreen, an important
creation figure.

*T*he Kombumerri were the original inhabitants of what is now known as the Gold
Coast. Their locality was bounded by the Coomera River to the north, the Tweed
to the south and the foothills of Mount Tambourine to the west. They were a part of
the larger Yugumbir Aboriginal group.

The present generation of Kombumerri people numbers about 150 (0.06 per cent
of the population of the Gold Coast). Living as they do in a rapidly growing area of
great tourist activity, they know that awareness of their culture and history — and
their stories — is vital to their survival as a people.

The love story which follows was told by the Aboriginal matriarch Ginny (Mc-
Gussey) Graham to her grand-daughter Hilma (Dillon) Blundell in 1940. Hilma was
about 12 at the time, and this story is a typical one for an Aboriginal girl entering
womanhood. The other two Kombumerri stories were recorded by white historians in
the earlier days of European presence in the Gold Coast.

Those star-crossed lovers of the Kombumerri love story,
the bulrush and the lily, on occasions still find a meeting
place. These young maidens and their admirers
keep their tryst hidden from the public gaze amid the
canefields of Gilberton.

Following Pages
Viewed here from the southern limits of the Wangerriburra
tribal territory, Wollumbin (Mount Warning) was, to the
Aborigines of Numinbah Valley, the father or patriarch of
mountains. To modern geologists it represents the throat
of a volcano that tapped a hot spot located deep inside the
earth's mantle. This hot spot lay far beneath the thick raft
of Australia's continental crust which had drifted across
above it, and through which, at Wollumbin, it burned a
hole to maintain an outlet at the surface.

A NERANG RIVER LOVE STORY

Along the way when we came close to water we would look out for Yimbun, the rush that grows around swampy sections of the river and in other wet places. Its flower is perched on top of a long stem and is brown and feels soft. I have always remembered when my mother told me how Yimbun came to grow near the water and always near the blue waterlilies. She heard this story told by Kombumerri women from the Gold Coast.

You see, a long time ago there was a young man and a young woman. They always went together and they would soon be married. She looked very beautiful. Every time they came close to the water, a bad spirit who lived in it became very jealous of the young man, and he decided to take the girl for himself. When he had taken her, he changed the girl into the blue flowering waterlilies, Muyim. This way he could always be reminded of her.

But the young man felt great grief at the loss of his companion. He searched for her along the water's edge where she had disappeared.

Even the bad spirit felt sorry for him. But he would not give back the young woman. So he took the man too, and changed him into Yimbun. In this way the young man could again be close to his woman, because both grow together, and in a breeze the tall Yimbun will bend over to be even closer to his woman, the blue waterlily.

With eerie accuracy the Aboriginal legend that tells of the creation of Wollumbin (Mount Warning) also tells of the reduction of storm-battered mountains to form the region's coastal plains. The region has indeed been carved by erosion from the flanks of a vast dome of volcanic lava centred on Wollumbin, a remnant of the volcano's main vent. Much of that erosion would have occurred during the storm-ridden episodes of glaciation that have characterised the last million years of the current ice age. These rolling plains near Beaudesert are a product of this — just as the story says.

WOLLUMBIN, NINGEROONGUN AND BARRAJANDA

Cougal's Cascades in Corrumbin Valley, southeastern Queensland, is one of many waterfalls that drain the remnants of what was once a vast dome of lava surrounding the volcanic vent called Wollumbin (Mount Warning). Much as the Aboriginal storytellers sensed, there had indeed been highlands here, a mountain of lava that stretched from Southport in Queensland, to Ballina in northern New South Wales. It has been torn apart by the storm water of 20 million years.

To the Aborigines of Numinbah Valley, Mount Warning was known as Wollumbin, "father, or patriarch, of mountains." Numinbah is one of the Aboriginal place names retained by the whites. Numinbah means "holding tight," from the notion that the narrow valley held the mountains tightly together.

The two eastern peaks of the Mount Warning or Wollumbin Range, were known to the Numinbah Aborigines as Ningeroongun and Barrajanda. How the peaks were named arose from the following legend from the Dreamtime. This story tells how the countryside of Beaudesert, considered to have once upon a time been mountainous, became flat.

Gwyala the hunter and his nephew Burrajum owned two greatly valued hunting dogs, Ningeroongun and Barrajanda. While away on an extended hunting trip the two Numinbah tribesmen and their dogs entered the

Logan territory. In pursuit of kangaroos, the two dogs ran well ahead of the two hunters.

The Logan natives heard the dogs barking and encircled them. Finding themselves in net, the dogs fought fiercely only to be eventually killed by the Logans. When Gwyala found Ningeroongun and Barrajanda dead, he wept.

"Don't cry, Uncle," said Burrajum. "I will cut vine."

Cutting vines was an essential part of the rain-making ceremony. In the Numinbah Valley, cutting of the piccabeen palm was part of the ceremony. Only certain men had this sort of authority and power. The Logan natives, upon seeing Burrajum do this, became afraid. The clouds gathered and it started to rain.

Rain continued to fall more and more heavily, day after day. The creeks and rivers rose to torrents. Great landslides scarred the mountainsides and buried all the people of the tribe. When the skies cleared, the once-mountainous country of the Logan had been reduced to little more than hillocks and plain.

In the meantime, Gwyala and Burrajum had taken the remains of Ningeroongun and Barrajanda over the big range to Wollumbin. There they buried the dogs, one under each of the two easterly peaks. Ever afterwards the peaks were known as Ningeroongun and Barrajanda.

This tale of the Dreamtime enjoins several laws: not to enter the territory of another tribe; not to covet the property of another tribe; above all not to kill a hunting dog.

Right
The cutting of piccabeen palms like these was a part of the rain-making ceremony of the Wangerriburra clan. Just such a ceremony performed by tribal ancestors was believed to have triggered rain storms that reduced the once mountainous country around Beaudesert to rolling plains.

The floodplain of the Logan River,
now devoted to sugarcane, was once the
rich food-gathering territory of the
Logan tribe. According to legend it was
their ancestors who, by killing two
valuable hunting dogs, caused this
once mountainous region to be flattened.

GWONDO THE DOLPHIN

Bottlenose dolphins.

Left:
Burleigh Head is the final resting place of Jabreen, the dreamtime creator of much of the Gold Coast landscape. His spirit sleeps inside the basalt headland with only his fingers, a cluster of hexagonal columns, showing near the summit on the eastern side.

Gwondo was the trainer of dogs. He would go out every day with his dogs, to teach them how to ambush the animals so all the tribe could eat. He had an elongated head, and his dark hair was interrupted by a crest of white hair that shone in the sunlight. It was just like the crest on the head of a cockatoo, only Gwondo's crest was white.

Wherever Gwondo went, his tribe could see him away in the distance on the hills, because his white hair would shine in the sunlight. The tribal elders would say to their children, "See, there is Gwondo and his dogs, searching for food for us all." Gwondo went hunting every day and he always came back to the camp with much food for his tribe. And all were very happy.

Now Gwondo grew old and as all mortals do, one day he died. The tribe mourned his loss, for he was much loved and the camp wailed many days and many nights.

Until one day the elders called to their children, "You have wailed enough for Gwondo. Now it is time to start thinking about living. Go down to the beach and be happy.

The children ran down to the beach and looked out to sea. Suddenly they all looked at each other, then turned and ran back to their elders, calling to them, "Come quickly, Gwondo, he is back with us. He is out in the sea."

The elders ran down to the beach and they nodded their heads and said, "Yes, it is Gwondo come back from his old Dreamtime to a new Dreamtime. He is now a dolphin and lives in the sea."

Now whenever you see a school of dolphins in the seas, look for the big old dolphin. You will recognise him because he has a large white fin on his back. He is Gwondo and he is training the young dolphins to chase fish close to shore so that his tribe will be able to catch them.

Gwondo is known to all tribes on the east coast of Australia. They call him their sea dog.

This pure stand of old cottonwood trees is at the
base of Burleigh Head. Unlike most flowers, these
cottonwoods, a species of hibiscus, gain colour only after
they have fallen. The flowers are edible and
would normally have been gathered by the young girls
of the tribe.

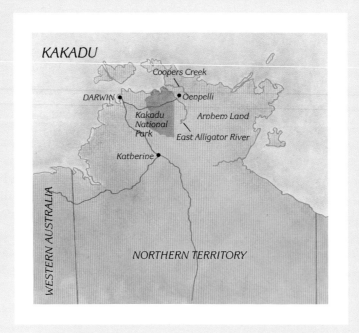

KAKADU

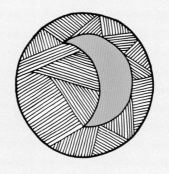

The view southeast
towards Nourlangie Rock.

*B*ill Neidjie is a senior representative of the Gagadju people, the once-populous group who belong to the Alligator Rivers region in the Northern Territory. This country has been continuously occupied for at least 60,000 years.

Bill Neidjie was born on the East Alligator River sometime after 1911. He spent most of his childhood in his father's country, Bunitj Clan land, on the western side of the East Alligator River, and learnt to live on bush tucker and manage the resources of his environment. His male relatives taught him the Aboriginal law. For two years he attended school at Oenpelli Mission.

As an adult Bill has worked at a variety of jobs: a short period of buffalo hunting, some timber milling, cleaning houses and cutting grass in Darwin, gathering man-grove wood for fuel, and about thirty years of loading luggers along the north coast. In 1979 Bill returned to his clan land permanently, to actively care for it.

As a result of the Alligator Rivers Stage I and Stage II Land Claims, Bunitj people's traditional ownership of land was recognised and title to their land was vested in the Kakadu and Jabiluka Land Trusts. Through the Land Trusts they are leasing their land back to the Commonwealth as a part of Kakadu National Park, which they jointly manage and protect. Bill is employed as a park ranger, and has become widely known for his writing.

The stories presented here come from the book *Story About Feeling*, a collection of talks Bill had with Keith Taylor in 1982, which were recorded and edited by Keith and published by Magabala Books in 1989. Keith has not attempted to explain or interpret Bill's story. As Bill says, "Someone can't tell you. Story e telling you yourself."

LAYING DOWN

Well I'll tell you about this story,
about story where you feel…laying down.

Tree, grass, star…

because star and tree working with you.

We got blood pressure

but same thing…spirit on your body,

but e working with you.

Even nice wind e blow…having a sleep…

because that spirit e with you.

Listen carefully this, you can hear me.

I'm telling you because earth just like mother

and father or brother of you.

That tree same thing.

Your body, my body I suppose.

I'm same as you…anyone.

Tree working when you sleeping and dream.

This story e can listen carefully, e can listen slow.

If you in city well I suppose lot of houses,

you can't hardly look this star

but might be one night you look.

Have a look star because that's the feeling.

String, blood…through your body.

Blue lily.

Left
The crocodile-infested East Alligator
River and its fertile floodplain helps to
support the largest concentration of
wetland fauna in Australia. It is also
home to storyteller Bill Neidjie and his
people, the Bunitj, of northern Kakadu.

Previous pages
The combined floodplains of the South
and East Alligator Rivers supports the
greatest concentration of waterbirds in
Australia. Each summer the shrinking
billabongs become the gathering places
for huge flocks of them, especially
magpie geese, who use the time feeding
and mating in preparation for the
monsoon floods. The density of these
flocks used to make them easy prey and
a ready source of food for the people
of the plains.

53

Finely tuned by necessity to the
dramatic seasonal changes of their
monsoonal environment, the people of
Arnhem Land learnt to regulate every
detail of their lives according to its
rhythms. Their calendar defines six
seasons in each year, each demanding
a distinctive human response. April,
for example, represents the season
of abundance, of tall grasses and
'knock-em-down' storms.

That star e working there…see?

E working. I can see.

Some of them small, you can't hardly see.

Always at night, if you lie down…

look careful, e working…see?

When you sleep…blood e pumping.

So you look…e go pink, e come white.

See im work? E work.

In the night you dream, lay down,

that star e working for you.

Tree…grass…

I love it tree because e love me too.

E watching me same as you

tree e working with your body, my body,

e working with us.

While you sleep e working.

Daylight, when you walking around, e work too.

That tree, grass…that all like our father.

Dirt, earth, I sleep with this earth.

Grass…just like your brother.

In my blood in my arm this grass.

This dirt for us because we'll be dead,

we'll be going this earth.

This the story now.

Crocodile. Unknown artist, Western
Arnhem Land, 1960s.

Following page
Aborigines have successfully shared the
wetlands of Kakadu with one of the
world's most dangerous predators, the
estuarine crocodile, for much of the last
50,000 years. It was an intimate yet
comfortable relationship, hinged on
mutual respect as well as the Aborigines'
shrewd bushcraft and accurate grasp of
their place within the ecological scheme
of things. It was also a relationship
maintained by the fact that those
who took it too much for granted
usually failed to survive.

Stone e never move

Rock e don't move round,

e got to stay for ever and ever.

E'll be there million, million…star.

Because e stay, e never move.

Tree e follow you'n'me,

e'll be dead behind us but next one e'll come.

Same people. Aborigine same.

We'll be dead but next one, kid, e'll be born.

Same this tree.

Star e'll stay for ever and ever.

When you laying down in the night, look that star.

I was. I look star.

I remember back when I was young.

That three there…*

That's the one crocodile!

That crocodile e float there and e look.

E said…

   "I'll get im that middle one."

Canoe…stringybark canoe.

E watching that middle man there,

sitting down middle, feeling sick…

   "I'll get im, kill im that middle one!"

*In the Orion constellation.

55

So that bark, that canoe, e tip over.

E got that man in the middle because e was sick.

See right hand side; three again there?

That crocodile e's got im now.

So e bright-up little bit more.

They used to tell us…

"Look that moon, middle of it…

that man and dog!

Good eye…

you can look one dog, one man up there.

That's the story for you so e can look.

If not…

well e can look that man when you sleep.

You dream."

"Yes… I can see little bit black there.

Yes, dog and man, arm with spear,

walking and dog behind."

"When you go hunting you want dog.

Well that's the dream over there."

One dog and one man you can look.

Slow you can look.

Because that man e had own spear, own womerra,

I think fire-stick and might be goose-wing.

You can't hardly see goose-wing now

because people this time…matches!

Before…they put goose-wing there.*

You know, might be in the wet**

you got to cook fire so e burn quick.

You cook anything and come back home.

Old people I said…

"Why you carry wing?"

"Because that story up there; have a look!"

They used to lay down…look that moon.

Moon. Moon is man. E said…

"People…they'll come back,

like I'm doing."

And Native-cat, e said…

"No!

We'll do other way.

We can dead*…never come back!"

So everyone they jump up.

They was burning him,

burning him with fire nearly killing him.

So e got every spot!

Some of the art in the rock shelters of Kakadu is in a style that appears to belong to a different people who lived in a very different environment. One painting in an upper gallery at Ubirr shows seven running men depicted in this spare fluid style, which is known as Mimi. Several factors suggest that it belongs to what is known as the pre-estuarine period, an era that came to an end when sea-levels rose some 7,000 to 9,000 years ago.

*Forewing of a goose used as
a fan to make draft in
wet conditions.

**The wet-season of heavy
monsoonal rains.

*Can die, be mortal.

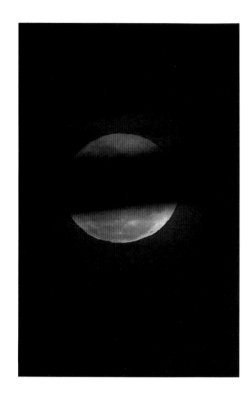

Moon make good.

He said, "Well they'll come back alive."

So e can look moon is finished

but e still come back.

We…we'll come to earth,

we'll be like earth.

E can see moon because e's changing it.

E go dark but e come back new…you got light.

Close on west side e can see new moon.

E go middle of the year, top,

middle night…e go middle age.

E go low…e getting little bit old now,

grey hair like me.

E go that moon just about daylight

and e comes out half-way…

e feeling sick.

E say…

   "Well I nearly finished!"

E getting old now,

right down with a walking stick.

Next morning, early, you can't see…

that mean e's finished.

That's the one e come back…

   "New moon!"

Following page

The beautiful Red Lily Lagoon lies near
the heart of Bill Neidjie's home country.
To the north is the floodplain of the East
Alligator River and resting among the
giant red lilies of the lagoon lies the
sandstone embodiment of its creator, the
ancestral spirit being, Indjuwanydjuwa.

E come back like young,

just like baby when they born.

E not moon but man himself.

So e turn…e went up there.

E dead but e come back.

We spoil it…

That Native-cat…

no-good, silly man!

Because they used to tell im story like that.

I never see im now…bit rough.

You stand there and quiet everybody.

They used to tell me…

"That's true story, now you got to keep it.

If someone e got to ask you, you tell im.

No-matter fifty, two hundred,

they'll listen to you.

Stand middle and tell.

E go might be thousand million,

million, million year.

E can't wear out…moon.

Star…about million, million year,

e'll still be there.

We... we gone

but youngest they come."

Because all that story up there

and here, all this dream here,

that's the one up there.

Star up there but here e made something...

rock or billabong or might be river.

That way star there.

I can touch if e close... but too far, e can see.

E can have a look nice lovely night,

all clear without cloud... but that for us.

Earth and star, sky, cloud, tree, animal...

I can listen over there flying-fox.

Coming out in the night eating his dinner or supper.

E looking for in the night, e allowed in the night

looking for something to eat.

E can't come daytime because im very shy.

In dream e made that womerra.

That way you see his claw-foot

hanging down other way.

Because that spirit for us... same as im.

E was man but we call im Gullumban...

that flying-fox now.

A native bee homes in on the fragrant heart of a blue lily to begin again the endless cycle of reproduction. The honey-loaded hives of these bees were the major source of sugar in the Aboriginal diet. The lily too, was a food source for the local people who used almost every part of it.

62

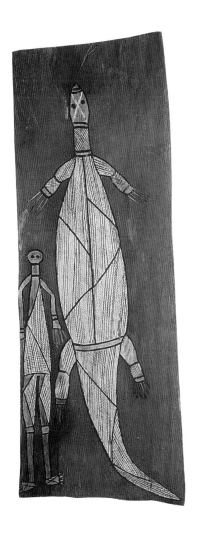

Lizard and Mimi spirit. Unknown artist,
Western Arnhem Land.

Following pages
Jim Jim Gorge.

That flower we call im Warrgarr, that his feed.

E eating his food in the night till daylight.

Just about daylight e not there

because e'll have to give im chance now honey-bees.

Bush-honey-bees e go get that flower.

Each flower e get half, half.

E make wax and we get honey then,

nice clean honey.

So that way flying-fox e work.

When you in 'business' you can't touch flying-fox.

You can't eat when you young.

They used to tell us…

"Don't eat that!"

Even water-python, grey one.

We never eat that.

But all, each animal got 'business'.

They got story each.

That white-chest eagle,

that's the one we say e can go billabong,

e can go salt-water

but that proper big one…black one!

E can go dry land and rock country.

63

All black. Sometimes little bit spot, yellow

but proper black one.

E can kill im black wallaby,

Black kangaroo that eagle can kill im.

We brought up like all the animal and bird

because eagle e fly round or might be jabiru,

might be brolga, might be goose.

Leichhardt's grasshopper.

Goose good eating. You got to eat goose

because goose e breed up again.

Soon as wet, e got to make egg…good eating.

Or goanna or long-neck turtle…

brought up because for us to eat.

Long-neck turtle you got to eat

but e get plenty again, e breed up more.

Even goanna e'll breed again.

Geese…e can eat two-hundred but e'll come.

E breed up here, egg…

another plain, another plain, another plain.

You might get one thousand and thousand goose.

Crow…e was eating this rubbish.

So e said…

  "Go on, get out!"

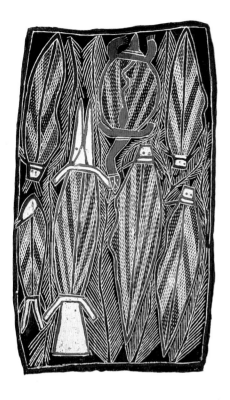

Eel-tail catfish, long-necked turtles, long tom fish and catfish. Alex Djirrgululu, Central Arnhem Land, early 1980s.

Following pages

The East Alligator River descends from the Arnhem plateau to the floodplains of Kakadu through a maze of crumbling rock towers that often convey an eerie sense of decaying architecture.

E man alright.

That hawk, all them…men

but they went* to all the bird, animal.

Any animal…we came from this world with the story.

You know, e had story with us.

Animal they come out in the night…insect

because e made up.

Some insect daytime but most in the night.

Some bird, I think owl,

e looking for something to eat in the night,

daytime you can't mostly look im.

Eagle hide in the tree or might be rock,

little bit of shelter where nobody can go,

quiet and having a sleep.

If somebody there, e listen, e go other place.

Any animal e change it place

because e might listen noise…

e don't like it.

But all that animal for this world.

Same us people.

*They turned into their animal forms.

67

Wind for us.

That way e come blow wind

and you feel it lovely, nice,

feel it cold now...lovely.

And I love it that wind.

That wind is wind for anybody...no-matter who.

Sometimes when you feeling you like outside

you might say...

   "I camp out there, camp outside

   and I might go sleep."

I like im.

I like im camp outside

because of course you got to sleep outside,

you got to feel im that wind and look star!

And that wind e blow, blow, blow, blow

and e can listen leaf

and you feeling yourself,

your body yourself,

you feeling...

   "Ahh...good sleep! I'll listen that wind."

Because e talking to you I suppose.

You go sleep. E say...

   "Well you might good sleep."

I feel it that wind, e coming slow...there!

Sometimes strong wind e blow strong, strong...

Some they might say...

   "What for e blow strong wind?"

Because e blow wind

because e's yours.

Not for yours yourself...

for anybody.

Rainbow Serpent painting at Ubirr.

You feel it no wind...hot!

You'll be looking for wind,

no-matter this time fan they make im.

People used to camp...but hot!

   "Hey! Where this wind?

   Where this wind gone?"

That's why I'm outside.

Last night...oh, e blow wind.

Yes...

that's the one for anybody.

Left
This lily-filled pond near the South Alligator River lies in a granite cradle of unimaginable age. Here the Arnhem Escarpment has crumbled away to reveal the ancient foundations upon which it was built, foundations that were formed more than 2,000 million years ago.

Sculptured by wind and rain from the layered sandstones of the Arnhem plateau, these curious formations are remnants of the retreating escarpment east of Ubirr.

That tree now, feeling...

e blow...

sit quiet, you speaking...

that tree now e speak...

that wind e blow...

e can listen.

Eagle there!

It's alright...

e make you "oh"

and look across there,

e can look plain and water there longside

and you feel yourself

how your body.

72

We think.

Story we think about, yes.

Tree…yes.

That story e listen.

Story…you'n'me same.

Grass im listen.

You'n'me same…anykind.

Bird e listen…anykind, eagle.

E sit down. E want to speak eagle eh?

Im listen. You listen…eagle.

Because e put im through your feeling.

But for us eagle…

all same.

Listen carefully, careful

and this spirit e come in your feeling

and you will feel it…anyone that.

I feel it…my body same as you.

I telling you this because the land for us,

never change round, never change.

Places for us, earth for us,

star, moon, tree, animal,

no-matter what sort of a animal, bird or snake…

all that animal same like us. Our friend that.

Following page
Kombolgie sandstone, 1.5 billion years
old, forms the Arnhem Escarpment and
is dissected by the East Alligator River.

Blood mistletoe.

This story e can listen careful

and how you want to feel on your feeling.

This story e coming through you body,

e go right down foot and head, fingernail and blood…

through the heart.

And e can feel it because e'll come right through.

And when you sleep you might dream something.

You might dream moon,

or you might dream water, storm.

You might dream tree, wind…

Oh anything e can dream…that dream e's true.

You having a sleep

but your spirit over there where you dream.

Daylight…e come back.

Now I telling story I can listen this.

You listen that wind e come more.

Tree e start moving round and feeling.

Intermediate egret.

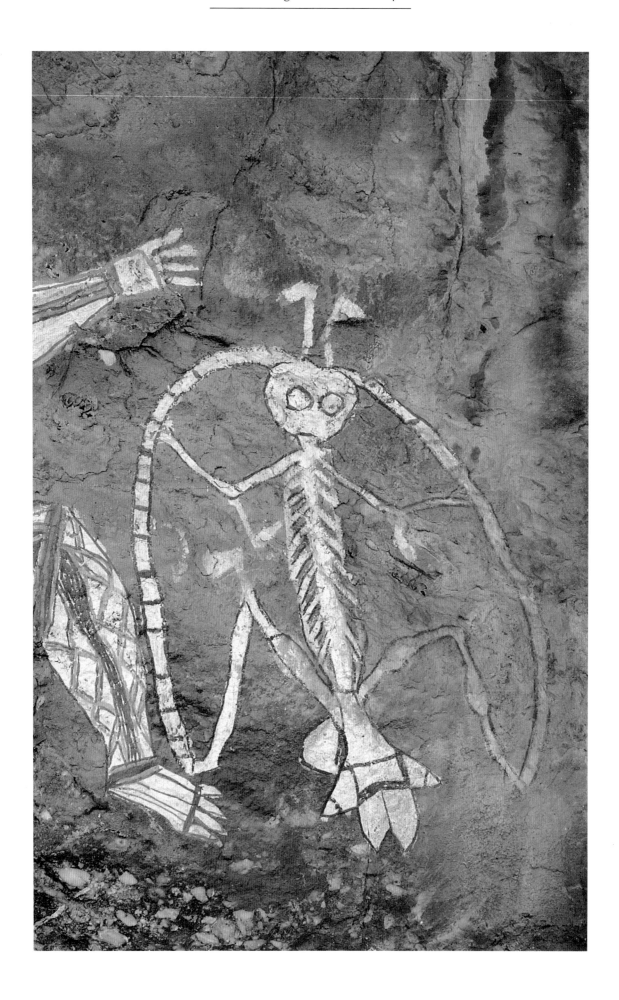

RAIN

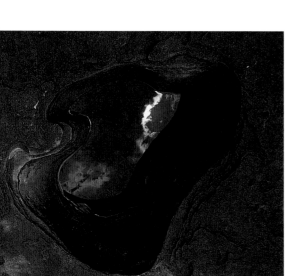

Rockhole, Jim Jim Creek.

Left
With stone axes attached to his head,
elbows and knees for making thunder,
Namarrgun the Lightning Man played a
vital role in the annual monsoon cycle on
which all life depended.

Following page
Twin Falls Gorge, Arnhem Escarpment.

*S*ky…
this cloud for us.
Your story, my story.

Yes anybody can see cloud

because e bring new water,

making more new water for us.

Rain for us, anybody.

Rain e give us because something.

Water for us.

Rain e'll come down because Warramurrauungi said that.

We can't be going dry, dry…

because that lightning e give us water.

That Woman done it.

What e do rain?

E raining because e give us something

new…what you eating it.

Yam, fish, anykind animal e give you…wet-season.

E drop im something there because story.

You can find good barra in the wet or after the wet

because that water.

Water running down in the stream...

Big-barra e follow that fresh-water.

Big-barra e travel, e come, keep going, get in fresh...

   "Oh fresh here! Keep going, can't stop."

Because shallow part e lay and drop.

E want that fresh.

Big-barra from salt-water.

Because... rain helping.

Something made there.

E can make eggs, mussels, anykind

but must have rain!

If you can't get rain what happen to us?

Something be happen!

You must get im because Law says you get rain.

E changing it now.

All this tree e changing it new leaf

because e got to come new rain.

Same any sort of a plant... e coming up new.

Yam e'll come too.

Yam, creeper, any bush-creeper e's growing

because that meaning of that Woman and that Man.

They made story

and this King-Brown.

They said...

   "This e got to grow each year before wet."

From their painted galleries high among the sandstone outliers of Ubirr the tribal artists of old could spend their monsoon afternoons in comfort as they watched the stormclouds gather along the Arnhem Escarpment. Ubirr contains one of the richest assemblies of ancient art in all the world.

One rain…you look grass e come.

E got something this top water here,

e throw something there.

First rain one, each billabong e drop down dry.

E want that new water so fish, turtle,

e can make new one.

E come along wet…e go dry.

Because that dry, e make im dry, e said…

"People be staying inside

and dry be going out for hunting.

82

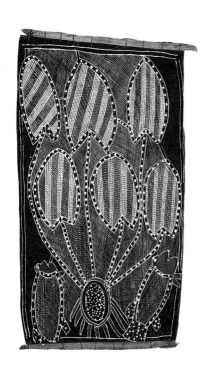

Waterlilies and freshwater fish at the sacred waterhole. Mick Wungulba, Western Arnhem Land, mid-1980s.

They can eat, look animal.

E looking for himself.

Snake…e can find himself because story.

Little lizard, little bird…

e looking for something to eat."

Snake or anykind…wet.

Blue-tongue lizard…no-matter what is animal, we animal,

we human being but this the story now.

Any sort of a animal…same we.

Animal not himself…we too.

We might look around

because that dream e started looking for.

E said…

"Well you must go get your fruit or honey

or something to eat, keep you alive.

Water e'll come down give you new fresh water."

That way first rain.

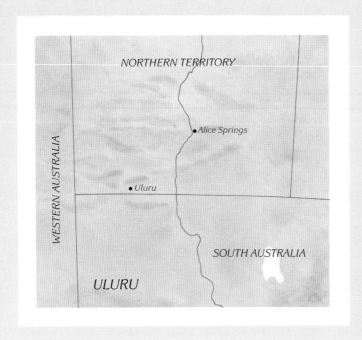

NORTHERN TERRITORY

• Alice Springs

WESTERN AUSTRALIA

• Uluru

SOUTH AUSTRALIA

ULURU

U L U R U

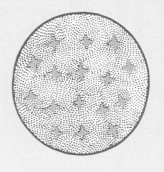

Uluru exerts an enormous influence on the daily
lives of its traditional custodians, and its
significance, like that of Katatjuta, is recognised
across most of arid Australia. It represents the
embodiment of seven of the most significant
creative spirits of their totemic faith.

Mutitjulu is the name of the community of Pitjantjatjara people who live at Uluru.

In 1985, they were granted inalienable freehold title to their traditional land which they have leased to the Commonwealth of Australia as a national park. They form a vital part of the management team of Uluru National Park, and they worked with the Australian National Parks and Wildlife Service to produce these versions of traditional Tjukurrpa (Law) stories to help visitors to their country understand its origins.

Itjaritjari, Mala, Kurpany, Kuniya and Liru and others helped to give Uluru the shape and significance that it bears today.

The Mala, or rufous hare wallaby, was once common
throughout western central Australia and provided both
a regular food source and one of the principal totemic
associations for the clans that hunted there. Like all the
other medium-sized marsupials of the region it was
unable to cope with the combined impact of domestic
livestock, rabbits, cats and foxes, however, and appears
to be headed for extinction.

Previous pages

Kandju Gorge, Uluru

THE MALA STORY

*I*n the beginning, Mala* men, women and children must travel a long way from the west and the north to reach Uluru. When they arrive they camp at separate sites from one another in groups of young men; old men; young and single women; and old and married women. They do this because they are here for Inma (a spiritual ceremony).

Some Mala men, who come from the west, carry the ceremonial pole, Ngaltawata. They scramble quickly to the top of Uluru and plant the pole in the ground at the northwest corner to begin the Inma. From this moment on, everything becomes a part of the ceremony. Even everyday jobs like: hunting; gathering and preparing food; collecting water; talking to people; or just waiting, are now done in a proper way for ceremony. This has become Law for men, women and children ever since.

The Mala are happy and busy. Suddenly people from the west come with an invitation to join another Inma. The Mala must refuse, as they have already started their own ceremony. The people from the west return home in great anger at the insult. They plan to wreak vengeance upon the Mala in a terrible way.

Across the land comes an evil, black, dog-like creature: Kurpany. He has been created by these people in the west to destroy the Mala ceremony. Lunpa, the kingfisher bird, cries a warning to the Mala. It is ignored, and Kurpany attacks and kills many Mala men, women and children. In terror, the remaining Mala flee to the south with Kurpany chasing them all the way.

A Mala is a rufous hare wallaby.

Mutitjulu, the permanent waterhole tucked in against the
southern flanks of Uluru, was the setting for the
legendary battle between the poisonous snake spirits from
Katatjuta and the ancestors of the local pythons. The pool
is fed primarily from above where there is another
rockhole said to be the home of a giant water python.
Water flowed down the gully into Mutitjulu whenever
this slumbering water spirit became aroused.

Previous pages
Although some of the domes of Katatjuta are taller,
monolithic Uluru tends to dominate the surrounding
plains, particularly at sunrise and sunset. Inevitably
perhaps, it provided the nomadic hunter-gatherers of
the desert plains with a cornerstone for their totemic
beliefs and a spiritual symbol of great power. As a mecca
for the modern tourist its drawing power now reaches
around the world.

THE MUTITJULU STORY

93

J. C. WOMBEY, AUSCAPE INTERNATIONAL

A species commonly identified under the heading Liru, or poisonous snakes, is the western brown. Fast-moving and aggressive, it is found throughout arid Australia, and legends of the Liru and their aggression are similarly common in the mythologies of many Aboriginal tribes.

Kapi Mutitjulu is the only reliable waterhole at Uluru, and has been used by Pitjantjatjara people for thousands of years. All of the features in the Mutitjulu area of Uluru are associated with the creation activities of a group of closely connected ancestral beings, the most important of which are two snakes, Kuniya and Liru. Wherever you walk in this area, you are surrounded by the presence of the Kuniya and Liru Tjukurrpa.

In the beginning, the female Kuniya becomes very angry after being publicly insulted by her nephew, Liru. She attacks him, in a great rage, and the battle becomes a disastrous encounter.

As Kuniya approaches Liru in her righteous anger, she performs a ritual dance to make it publicly known that a woman of power is seeking to punish the person who has insulted her. Kuniya is furious, and in an attempt to control the dark forces that her ritual anger is unleashing, she picks up a

D. PARER AND E. PARER-COOK. AUSCAPE INTERNATIONAL

The woma, or black-headed python of central Australia
appears to be one of two or three species that the desert
tribes knew as Kuniya, the harmless ones. The principal
home of the Kuniya was believed to be around Mutitjulu
on the southern side of Uluru. The woma has been
known to grow almost three metres long.

Previous pages
Geological evidence suggests that the domes of Katatjuta
(The Olgas) and Uluru (Ayers Rock), which is just visible
on the horizon, are remnants of a vast bed of rubble
that accumulated along the northern flanks of a
2,000-kilometre chain of alps some 550 million years ago.
Prized though they are in the modern mythology of
international tourism and the glossy magazine, it is
a slight thing compared to their significance for the tribal
custodians of Australia's desert regions.

handful of sand and lets it fall to the ground. This is to settle the forces she is disturbing, so that they will not harm others.

However, Kuniya's rage is too strong, and a great battle takes place. Kuniya strikes Liru and he receives a small wound as he deflects the blow with his shield. Then Kuniya delivers Liru a second strike and he receives a deep, long and fatal wound. Liru's shield falls with him to the ground.

Kuniya has avenged her honour, but in her furious rage every plant near the battle has become poisoned. The spearwood bush here is particularly poisoned.

Evidence of Kuniya's actions as she rushes towards her insulter and destroys him, is clear in the features of Uluru, and celebrated today in story, song and ritual dance.

Following pages
Deep caves carved into the sides of Uluru have long
provided valuable refuge for both animal and human in
this relatively ungenerous and uncertain environment.
Every major recess has now acquired a specific totemic
sequence and an appropriate name. Caves at the left of
this picture were also traditionally reserved for exclusive
use by women of the tribe

Flinders Island
Bass Strait
Babel Island
Furneaux
Group
Cape Barren
Island
Penguin
Toorbunna
(Mount Ben Lomond)
Launceston
Cradle Mountain
South Esk River
Great
Lake
Lake Saint Clair
Oyster
Bay
Big River
Tribe area
HOBART
Tasman Peninsula
TASMANIA

T A S M A N I A

The view west from
Cradle Mountain.

*J*im Everett, born on Flinders Island off the northeast coast of Tasmania, is a
Tasmanian Aborigine from the Ben Lomond Tribe, the Plangermairreenner people,
midway down the east coast of Tasmania. Jim was influenced by his friend Oodgeroo
Noonuccal to take an Aboriginal name similar to hers. His name of Pura-Lia Meenamatta means "paperbark from the Ben Lomond area".

Jim has written for as long as he can remember — poetry, short stories and theatre
pieces. He has had a long involvement in Aboriginal politics and served two terms as
the elected state secretary of the Tasmanian Aboriginal Centre, a community-based
political organisation.

He has also served on the Aboriginal Arts Board of the Australia Council, and was
the first producer to the ABC's Aboriginal TV Unit in Sydney. In 1988, Jim produced
a film about the Aboriginal anti-bicentennial march in Sydney, titled "One People
Sing Freedom".

Jim has written these stories on the basis of knowledge within the Tasmanian
Aboriginal community and his personal research and understanding of the Aboriginal
stories of the past. Jim says, "These stories represent the contemporary legends of the
Tasmanian Aboriginal people, and although they are not stories from our tribal people
they have the status of being our stories. It is necessary to understand that Aborigines
are only at the beginning of literary expression. I am pleased to be able to express my
people's stories by using what creative skills I have to bring it all together."

In these stories you, the reader, will get to know the Aboriginal community in
Tasmania as it is now, in its own reality.

Both Lake Saint Clair and Mount Ida were the by-products
of glaciers carving their way from Tasmania's ice-bound
central plateau to the sea between 16,000 and 20,000
years ago. It would have been a time of bitter cold and
considerable hardship for the first Tasmanians who then
represented the frontiers of human expansion and
its southernmost advance.

Following pages
Tasmanian environments have undergone drastic changes
during the past 30,000 years. At the height of the last
glacial era some 18,000 years ago, this mossy myrtle
forest near Cradle Mountain did not exist. The Cradle
Mountain region then lay beneath a permanent ice-sheet
that covered the whole of central Tasmania.

BALLAWINNE (RED OCHRE)

The day was a dull early-winter's day in Tasmania on the edge of the foothills of Cradle Mountain. A car door slams and a man's voice is heard, "This is the area Barbara, our tribal lands were centred around this mountain."

A young woman's voice replies, "Well, tell me the story Dad, you know I want to hear it all, what was our tribal people like?" Barbara is a small-boned teenager with big green eyes and wavy red hair, she sits on a rock and looks intently at her father.

"Our band was of the Big River Tribe," he said, "the band was called the Luggermairrernerpairrer."

"Gosh that's a long name Dad, I don't think I can say it," Barbara said.

"Yeah it's long alright," her Dad replied, "and hard to say…anyway, our band had the best tracks of all, we could move from Cradle Mountain here, all the way up past Lake Saint Clair and even to the Great Lakes area."

He continued, "Way back before, even before the Giant Fish came and ate the land to make what is now known as Bass Strait, our tribe had the only ochre mine of all the tribes." Barbara's dad picked up a stick and then sat on a tree stump. He was a tall slim man with reddish brown hair, he too had green eyes, yet unlike his daughter he had a dark complexion. He began doodling in the dirt with the stick, drawing a map of the Big River tribal lands. "Yes, we had a big mine somewhere on Cradle Mountain, and the other tribes would trade with us for the ochre.

"One day the Oyster Bay Tribe was trading with the Big River Mob when an argument started over who owned the ochre, the Oyster Bay fullas wanted more ochre, and for no cost. Well, while the leaders are right into the argument, a young fulla from the Oyster Bay Mob sneaks round the back of everyone and steals a big lump of red ochre."

"Gee Dad," says Barbara, "what happened when he did that?"

"Ho! The Big River Mob went mad when they seen what was happening, and gave chase quick smart. But this fulla was real fast and they couldn't catch him. The fastest of the Big River runners were able to keep him in sight, but they couldn't get up to him."

"But Dad," says Barbara, "surely a lump of ochre wouldn't be that important?"

"Oh yes it would!" he said. "That lump of red ochre was all that was left from the mine, and it was very important because it could multiply if broken into smaller lumps and thrown on to the ground." Barbara laughed at this, and said, "No wonder them fullas were mad Dad, anyway, go on, tell me more."

"Well that lad ran all over the Big River tribal lands, even as far as the Ben Lomond tribal lands. He was breaking off little pieces of ochre and dropping it, hoping that his pursuers would stop to pick the pieces up. He was hopin' to slow'm down."

"Did his trick work Dad?" asked Barbara.

"No, but it did leave a trail of ochre all over the place. Anyway, he finally found a way out of the Big River lands and led his chasers all over the north of the island, still breaking off pieces of ochre to drop as decoys.

"So after a while he can see he's almost out of ochre, and still they chase him, so he runs in a circle and back into the Big River land. In fact where he

Pencil Pines, Dove Lake and Cradle Mountain.

ran through into Big River country is now known as Saint Peter's Pass."

Barbara asked, "Did they catch him, Dad?"

"No, he was too smart, he jumped into Lake Saint Clair and swam around in deep water until eventually the Big River spirit Warrawa turned him into a freshwater crayfish as punishment for stealing the ochre.

"Later on that smart fulla, now a crayfish, sneaked out of the lake at night and went down the mountain in a small creek. He lived for years makin' more crayfish to live in the creeks that run into Bass Strait.

"Anyway," Barbara's dad continued, "there was now ochre all over the north people's lands, and as the rain came the ochre grew to be new ochre mines. Ballawinne, our old people called it, means 'red ochre'. Now the northern tribes had their own ochre, and could trade with the southern tribes for all sorts of things."

Barbara was thoughtful, and said, "I think that was a good way for things to end. Pity about the fulla who stole the ochre, but it did help a lot of people get some ochre, didn't it Dad?"

"Yep," he replied, "it sure did. Our ancestors left us with two important things because of the ochre bein' stolen: that's the ochre of course; and now we can get crayfish from all of the creeks that run into Bass Strait."

"Yeah, well come on Dad, let's drive up to that creek outside of Penguin* and catch a feed of crays to take home, Mum loves'm."

*Penguin is a small town in the north of Tasmania.

Left
Like giant funerary poles, dolerite pillars like these crest many of the ridgelines in the mountain wilderness of western Tasmania. They once helped to define the boundaries of the Big River people who roamed the central highlands for more than 20,000 years.

When these dead Tasmanian myrtle trees began life as seedlings on the banks of Lake Saint Clair, European eyes had not yet sighted Australian shores. Meanwhile Tasmania's first settlers had already lived there for at least 30,000 years. Traces of human occupation found in a rock shelter only 60 kilometres to the east have been dated to around 30,800 years ago.

THE MOON AND THE SNAKE

*I*t was a dark night in Hobart as Joan made her mother a cup of tea. June, Joan's mother, was down from the Cape Barren Island for a visit. She liked to be in the city sometimes just to know the comforts that were not everyday on the island.

With a cuppa each they sat on the verandah looking over the city. It was a still night and quite warm. They were yarning away about all sorts of things, the old coes* on the islands, where family were now, all that kind of talk.

All of a sudden, a blackout hit their part of the city, the lights went out and all seemed quite eerie. The two women stopped talking, and seemed to enjoy the quiet of the night in darkness around them.

Just then the moon came out from behind a cloud and lit up the night, and at the same time a shooting star went right across the sky. June said to her daughter, "This reminds me of the story of the moon and the snake, an old story from our tribal people, I've heard the old coes tell it often."

"Tell me the story will yuh Mum?" says Joan. "Okay," June said, and on she went. "This story is about the Ben Lomond area, the Meenamatta area. The people were known as the Plangermairrener, that's out family's mob.

---

*Old coes *is an island slang meaning "old coves", coming from seamen's slang meaning "mate". Used mainly by Cape Barren Islanders and the people on Flinders Island, the non-Aboriginal islanders use it also.*

According to legend these mist-shrouded crags were
heaved up from below during an underground fight
between an Aboriginal woman and a snake spirit. The
geological story has a similar ring to it in that Toorbunna
(Mount Ben Lomond) represents a huge reservoir of
molten lava that was injected into an underground
fault system when the region came under strain as
Australia and Antarctica first began to pull apart
175 million years ago.

There were three bands in the Meenamatta area, the other two were known as the Plindermairhemener band and the Tonenerweenerlarmenne Band, but they're all our mob anyway," said June.

"There was a foxy old snake lived in the ground at that place, and there was this real cheeky little Aboriginal woman called Puggareetya who was always tryin' to play tricks on Loiena, that was the snake's name."

Joan was laying back in the beanbag now, just listening, June had finished her tea, and putting the cup on the verandah floor, she continued.

"One day Puggareetya sneaked up on Loiena, who was sleeping in the sun, and grabbed his tail and began to pull the snake away from his home. Now Loiena's home was a hole in the ground, it was very flat where the Plangermairrener people lived, and Loiena had the only home underground.

"Anyway," June went on, "Loiena didn't wake up as Puggareetya dragged him away from his home, and she dragged him to a big rock and hid him behind it. Then, Puggareetya ran back to Loiena's hole and went inside to see what other mischief she could get up to."

Joan laughed softly and said, "That Puggareetya was sure a cheeky one alright."

"Yes," laughed June, "sure was, but Loiena woke up while Puggareetya was in his home, he looked around and guessed straight away that Puggareetya had dragged him to the rock. Loiena was angry and quickly slithered to his hole in the ground, in he went and caught Puggareetya inside."

"Crikey Mum," exclaimed Joan, "what happened then?"

"A big fight started and the ground began to heave and lift, they fought so hard that they made the land lift way up until a mountain was made, the people called that mountain Toorbunna. We call it Mount Ben Lomond now of course."

June went on, "The fight ended up outside the hole and Loiena was winning. Puggareetya quickly grabbed the big rock that she had dragged Loiena to, and hung on for life. Loiena was even more angry now, and using the powers of a snake spirit he flung Puggareetya high into the sky. So Mienteina, the sky spirit, grabbed both Puggareetya and the rock and kept them there."

June said, "Well that got rid of Puggareetya from mischief with Loiena, but what about the moon?"

"Oh, yes," said June. "The sky spirit, Mienteina, held the big rock so that the sun would shine on it from the other side of the earth, this made it light up at night time. Mienteina then turned the rock into a spirit called Weenah Leah, which means moon. Weenah Leah lives with Mienteina even to this day."

"What happened to Puggareetya, Mum?" asked Joan, really interested now.

"Mienteina didn't like Puggareetya — she still played her tricks in the sky. So every now and then Mienteina would grab Puggareetya and throw her through the sky. It's nights like this that Puggareetya can be seen, a shooting star whizzing through the sky."

Joan smiled and said in a teasing sort of voice, "And the land was quiet, and Loiena the snake was happy ever after."

"Not quite," said June. "Loiena got such a fright to see Weenah Leah shining so brightly, and Puggareetya shooting across the sky, that he began to thrash about. He wriggled and slid about so much that he made a deep channel in the ground." June looked to see if Joan was listening, and satisfied that she was, went on with the story. "That channel is what we now know as the South Esk River that runs off from Toorbunna, Mount Ben Lomond.

Toorbunna (Mount Ben Lomond).

Anyway Loiena dug another hole to live in, and they say he still lives inside Toorbunna as the snake spirit."

"Look! Did yuh see that, Mum?" exclaimed Joan. "A shooting star over there." Joan pointed excitedly. "Do yuh reckon that was Puggareetya?"

"Oh yes my girl, that'd be Puggareetya alright."

Just then the moon went behind a big cloud and it began to get very dark. Another shooting star shot across the sky, and all of a sudden the lights in the house came on. The two women looked at each other and smiled.

KUTI KINA

"Hoy! You jungins*, come away from there or Kuti Kina will come and get yuh!"

It was old Aunty Rya calling to a group of Aboriginal children who were climbing a big rock at the foot of Sharp Hill on Babel Island. Sharp Hill was the subject of many ghost stories told by the Aborigines who went mutton-birding on Babel Island each year. Aunty Rya believed that Kuti Kina lived there, protecting the spirits on Sharp Hill, and children should not disturb the spirits. The children respected Aunty Rya and did as they were bid, running down the hill to the sheds where their parents were working.

Muttonbirds are seabirds that have been a food resource of the Tasmanian Aboriginal people for more than 12,000 years. The muttonbird chicks are harvested from their burrows in the ground over a five-week season each year. This cultural activity is still carried on by today's Tasmanian Aboriginal community.

Anyway, Aunty Rya was doing her bit keeping the children out of trouble. One of the children, Larni, a light-haired boy with brown eyes, came down to where Aunty Rya was sitting.

"Is Kuti Kina an evil spirit Aunty Rya?" he asked with a frightened look on his face.

"Oh no my boy!" she said, "Kuti Kina is the protector of special places that belong to us."

*The spelling of the word jungins is correct. It represents the English slang of Tasmanian Aborigines on the islands, especially Cape Barren Island, second largest island of the Furneaux Group. Jungins means "youngsters."

"Why should we be frightened of Kuti Kina then?" said Larni.

"Sit down and I'll tell you all about Kuti Kina," replied Aunty Rya. Larni sat on an old kerosene tin next to Aunty Rya's hut and leaned back on the wall, enjoying the warmth of the sun. Aunty Rya began.

"A long time ago there was this Aboriginal woman named Mennuggana, her name meant 'black cockatoo', and she was always trying to learn about things around her.

"One day she was near the sacred caves, a place where only the spirit people in the tribe were allowed to go. But Mennuggana wanted to see what they looked like inside, so she crept close to the entrance of the biggest cave."

"Well what was in the cave?" asked Larni.

"The spirit people's art, hand stencils made by spitting ochre on a hand on the rock wall. Our Old People believed that the art would protect the cave spirit."

Aunty Rya continued with the story. "Anyway, as Mennuggana got close to the cave entrance a cold wind began to blow from the cave. Mennuggana got frightened as the wind blew harder."

Larni's eyes were big as the moon, he could see a picture in his mind of the wind blowing Mennuggana away from the cave. He asked, "Did the wind hurt Mennuggana, Aunty?"

"No, no, no boy!" she said. "The wind began to make a funny noise, then its voice could be heard, real loud…it said, 'GO AWAY WOMAN, THIS IS A SPIRIT PLACE.' Mennuggana knew it was the Great Ancestor speaking and she got so frightened that she ran into the cave to hide. The Great Ancestor was not pleased at Mennuggana going into the cave, and he sent a birdman down to get her."

BRIAN PRINCE

Sources of ochre for body decoration and rock art were
rare, and prized by Tasmania's Aborigines. They were
known to have dived to reach one source off the southwest
coast. Unfortunately, little remains of their art now. This
hand stencil is in Ballawinne Cave, on the Maxwell River.

Previous pages
The frequency of bushfires is a major factor in
determining the limits of Tasmania's rainforest areas.
While little is known about Aboriginal use of fire in
Tasmania it is likely that, as on the mainland, it played
a crucial role in shaping the distribution of fire-sensitive
myrtle forests like this one in Mount Field National Park.

123

Aunty Rya went on. "The birdman went to the cave and quickly carried Mennuggana off, and up to the Great Spirit. The Great Spirit was very angry, and said, 'YOU ARE TO BE PUNISHED FOR BREAKING THE LAW.' And a blaze of bright sunlight shone on Mennuggana."

Larni interrupted, "Gee Aunty, did the Great Ancestor kill Mennuggana?"

"Oh no my boy!" she exclaimed. "The sun is the giver of all life, no...the Great Spirit wouldn't use the sun like that. The sun turned Mennuggana into a spirit of the Great Ancestor."

"What sort'f spirit was Mennuggana turned into, Aunty?" said Larni with a look of awe on his face.

"Mennuggana was turned into Kuti Kina my boy, the spirit to protect the sacred places of our people. Kuti Kina was sent back to the land to keep the law."

"Gee Aunty, Kuti Kina is like the white people's Boogey Man, isn't it?" comes Larni speaking quite fast.

Aunty Rya thinks for a minute before answering. "I s'pose that's right, but you mind now that you don't go up Sharp Hill or otherwise Kuti Kina will get you, now off with yah."

Larni gets off his kerosene tin and runs over to where some of the children are playing chasey around the boxthorn scrub. "Hey!" Larni yells. "Aunty Rya just told me all about Kuti Kina, we better not go up Sharp Hill or Kuti Kina will come and take us to the Great Ancestor."

"Gosh, what'll the Great Ancestor do if that happens?" says Louana, the eldest girl in the group.

"The Great Ancestor will turn you into a spirit and make you protect Sharp Hill forever," says Larni.

That evening as the sun set, the group of Aboriginal children sat by the camp fire and looked up at Sharp Hill, a place where Kuti Kina watches over Babel Island.

NOTE: *Babel Island is one of the many islands in the Furneaux Group off the northeast coast of Tasmania. It was the most popular muttonbird island of the straits in post-war years, having a population of upwards of three hundred people for the then six-week season. Today it is becoming less used for muttonbirding, and is only catering for about twenty Aboriginal muttonbirders each season.*

Left
Tasmania's long isolation from the Australian mainland has imparted a distinctive character to much of its flora and fauna. Many Tasmanian species occur nowhere else. The elegant Tasmanian waratah is one of these. Although the mechanics of it were slightly different, a similar distinction arose between mainland Aborigines and their isolated island cousins. They too appear to have been unique.

Following page
A feature of the 'organ-pipe' coast of Tasman Peninsula is Remarkable Cave. Here the sea has eaten away a long, narrow slot of dolerite, leaving the overlying sandstone intact.

THE FISH SPIRIT

They were sitting around the deck of the *Christine Carol,* a 45-foot crayboat tied up at the wharf in Hobart. Talk was about their ancestors, the Old People, Tasmanian Aborigines. These young Aborigines were of course talking about Aborigines and fish, they being fish-catchers themselves.

Jamie, about 18 years of age with blond curly hair and a cheeky smile, was on the subject of the spirits. "My father reckons that Ria Warrawah the sea spirit made our Old People stop eatin' scale fish," he said with a rather intense look at the others.

His sister, Ebonee, quickly broke in. "I know what our tribal people called the fish spirit. Peeggana, that's what it's called," she said in a smug way.

An old voice drifted into the conversation just then, a quiet voice, it was Granpop Edgar. "Yuh know, I heard the story 'bout why the Old Fullas stopped eatin' fish," he said.

Rosie started to say, "How can we be sure that the spirits had anything to do with…" as Justin said in a loud voice, "I want to hear the story anyway, so just be quiet and let Granpop tell us about it."

"Well, it seems there were three sea spirits way back then. There was Peeggana and Nunnya, they were the fish spirit and the crayfish spirit. But the bad one was Ria Warrawah, the sea demon spirit." Granpop Edgar looked at the young ones and continued. "The tribes were eating mainly scale fish around then, along with emu and possums…and that kinda tucker…you know."

He puffed on his old blackwood pipe and went on. "A real cheeky young fulla called Maywerick was always fishin' close to where Ria Warrawah lived. Now Maywerick loved to eat scale fish, and he was friendly with Peeggana. Of course Ria Warrawah was Peeggana's worst enemy, because Ria Warrawah didn't like Peeggana lettin' Maywerick have *any* fish."

"Was Maywerick the fish-catcher for his people Granpop?" asked Ebonee.

"Yep!" said Granpop, "and everyone was happy and had plenty tucker, but they mostly sat around and just waited for Maywerick to bring the food."

Justin piped up, "Yuh mean they was lazy and didn't help to get the fish, Granpop?"

"That's right," said Granpop Edgar, "and the crayfish spirit, Nunnya, was always tryin' to get Maywerick to talk to the people about catching shellfish and crayfish because it would be good for their diet."

Old Granpop Edgar was warming to the subject now. He went on, "Now Ria Warrawah was so tired of what was goin' on that he decided one day to kill Maywerick. He sneaked around underwater to near where Maywerick had a big catch of fish, and before anyone could see what was happening Ria Warrawah threw a Neaggara Pe-na at Maywerick and killed him."

"What's a Neaggara Pe-na Granpop?" asks Rosie.

"It's a dream spear of the spirits my girl," Granpop gives the answer. "Yuh see, this Neaggara Pe-na, when it kills Maywerick, it brings his dream to life. Now as it happens Maywerick had often dreamed that his people would stop eating scale fish, and start eating lots of shellfish and crays and crabs and the like."

"Oh boy!" exclaims Jamie, "Yuh mean they stopped eatin' scale fish when the dream came true?"

Granpop Edgar laughed quietly at this, then said, "Well sort of I s'pose yuh could say…but it wasn't until Nunnya, who came along just after Maywerick was speared, and had a big fight with Ria Warrawah, that the dream started to be seen."

He puffed long and noisily on his pipe, and went on. "The water was boilin' from the fight, and the spirits were goin' mad. Just then along came Tiabeah, Maywerick's wife, who threw the big catch of fish that Maywerick had caught into the sea where the spirits were fighting. This made the spirits fight even more."

The young ones on the deck of the *Christine Carol* were silent with attention. Granpop continued the story. "Tiabeah was busy trying to bring Maywerick back to life, and as the two spirits fought, Peeggana the scale fish spirit grabbed both Maywerick and Tiabeah and carried them into the deep water never to be seen again.

"The people were very scared," Granpop went on, "and ran away from where Nunnya and Ria Warrawah were making the sea boil, and you know, our Old People never ate scale fish for hundreds of years after that."

Justin was quick to ask, "What happened to the spirits fighting, Granpop?"

"Oh…they still fight a lot, and yuh can see 'em on a windy day in the shallow water stirrin' up the sea. Yuh gotta be careful and respect the sea, 'specially when yuh go out fishin', that damn Ria Warrawah plays all sorts of tricks so be careful," he said in a tired voice.

He went on to say in a slow voice now, "The people started to catch lots of crayfish after that and dive for shellfish, and work very hard to see that everyone had enough food to live comfortable like."

The long list of Tasmanian
shipwrecks suggests that
Tasmania's rugged coastline is
exceptionally hazardous. Its rocky
shores are washed by swells that
have come half-way round the
world, while sudden storms like this
one off Tasman Peninsula add a
factor of unpredictability that well
justified the great caution with
which Tasmanian Aborigines seem
to have treated the sea.

Following page
Aboriginal artists conveyed their
messages with a formalised set of
symbols. Concentric circles usually
meant waterhole. This very old
engraving is at Devonport on the
central north coast.

Granpop got up from his deckchair and walked over to a big pile of ropes on the deck. He sat down on the ropes. "You should always remember that Ria Warrawah and Nunnya are still about, and if yuh spot the sea on the boil take your boat away from them, it's dangerous to go where they are, you could lose your boat.

"Anyway," he said, "Maywerick and Tiabeah are spirits now with Peeggana in the deep water, we don't see 'em any more. Now that these spirits are so busy fighting or hiding in the deep water…there are no spirits…to see our…fish are safe…from being caught out…altogether." Granpop Edgar laid back amongst the ropes and closed his eyes, he was falling asleep.

Just then Aaron, the youngest of the crew, stuck his head out of the fo'c'sle and yelled to the group, "Righto you fullas, got a good feed of fish cooked for lunch, come'n get it." Jamie yelled back, "What kinda fish did yah cook?"

"Some flathead, some perch and a couple of salmon," says Aaron, "come on or they'll get cold."

Almost as one the group yelled back at Aaron, "I'm not hungry!"

If anyone had cared to look at that very moment, they would have noticed a sneaky grin come over Granpop Edgar's face.

Right
Survival was rarely a problem for most Tasmanian tribes, at least until European colonisation began. In fact the larder could, on occasions, become overstocked, thanks to the highly evolved and opportunistic reproduction system of marsupials such as the Forester, or Eastern Grey Kangaroo, thinning here on Maria Island, part of the territory of the Oyster Bay Tribe.

Following page
Large shell middens scattered along the Freycinet Peninsula suggest that this spectacularly 'painted' coast was a popular summer resort for people of the Oyster Bay Tribe. The colour comes from a variety of lichens that thrive on the granite.

134

TONAH LEAH, THE FIRE SPIRIT

*I*t was a nice sunny day on the Tasman Peninsula. It was Christmas time and the campers were there in droves. Ben and Marge were there with their children, Tigh and Nicki. Tigh was tall for his age, 10 years, and Nicki was 13 years of age, a teenager to the bone.

There would be other Tasmanian Aborigines on holidays at the Peninsula even though Tigh and Nicki hadn't spotted anyone they knew, so far anyway.

"Come on kids, get some wood, we want a big fire tonight," said their father. Nicki was quick to help around the camp, and started off to get wood from the nearby scrub. Tigh hated the idea and walked around with his hands in his pockets.

"Aaww, come on Tigh," said Ben, "help Nicki get the wood, it's gettin' late." So Tigh forced himself to actually go and get some wood.

Later that evening the family sat around the camp fire and talked. "I always enjoy food cooked on a camp fire," said Marge.

"Me too!" from Tigh, who thought of food above all other things in life.

"Yeah, me too," said Ben thoughtfully. "Yuh know…this place is where the fire spirit first gave fire to our Old Fullas."

"You mean right here at our camp site Dad?" asked Nicki.

"No, I mean Tasman Peninsula, want to hear th'story?" offered Ben.

Tigh nodded, Marge and Nicki both said they would like to hear it. So, Ben started.

"Way back in the old days, way back when our tribal people were just beginning to learn the ways of life, there was hardly any light."

"No light! Even of a day Dad?" said Tigh.

"That's right mate, it was like dusk all the time. Anyway, our tribal band was called the Pydairrerme. They were part of what white people called the Oyster Bay Tribe."

Ben went on with the story. "Well, the Pydairrerme Band were great hunters, they hunted wallaby and emu, and dived for shellfish and crayfish. The trouble was that because there was no light, it was very cold, and the people did not know about fire.

"One day the Great Ancestor came to the land where the Pydairrerme lived, the Great Ancestor was in the form of the Lyekah, the firetail bird. The Lyekah perched in a tree near the camp of Kakannawayreetya, a brave hunter. Kakannawayreetya saw the Lyekah and quickly speared it."

"Crikey Dad, did this mean he killed the Great Ancestor?" queried Tigh.

"Not at all mate, you can't kill the Great Ancestor, it's a spirit that's always with us. But Kakannawayreetya didn't know it was the Great Ancestor, and he plucked the bird and tied its red feathers to his hair.

"It had made the Great Ancestor sad to see his people living in darkness. When the Lyekah was killed the Great Ancestor took the body of a white cockatoo, the Weeanoobryna. This made the Great Ancestor see the darkness even more."

Ben stopped for a minute and leaned over to grab the billycan of tea, he poured it into a tin mug and stirred some sugar in it. He sipped it before returning to the story.

"The Great Ancestor decided to help the people, and as the Weeanoobryna it flew at Kakannawayreetya and grabbed the red feathers from his hair. The Weeanoobryna flew round and round Kakannawayreetya, so fast that the red feathers got brighter and brighter."

Electrical Storm

Following pages
Much of Tasmania's southeast coast is characterised by
towering sea cliffs of vertically jointed dolerite. This
dolerite pillar at Cape Hauy on Tasman Peninsula is known
as the Candlestick. The sheer inhospitality of the coastline
would have done much to dissuade the Oyster Bay
people from off-shore fishing.

Ben drank some more tea, noting that his family were laying back, relaxed, but obviously listening. He went on, "The feathers got so bright that they started to burn, and the cockatoo began to singe, its feathers going black. There was fire everywhere around Kakannawayreetya, and it started to burn him, until all that could be seen was one big flame. It got so big that it lifted into the sky, making a sun and giving light to the land."

Ben finished his drink and hung the mug on a branch. He continued the story. "All of a sudden the cockatoo, now black with some of its tail feathers singed yellow, came out of the sun and flew over the people, it was still the Great Ancestor.

"The Great Ancestor spoke from the cockatoo, 'FROM NOW ON YOU WILL HAVE THE SUN TO GIVE YOU LIGHT AND WARMTH, BUT ALSO NIGHT WHICH IS DARK. KAKANNAWAYREETYA WILL BE YOUR TONAH LEAH FOREVER, YOUR FIRE SPIRIT, HE WILL GIVE YOU FIRE.'

"The blackened cockatoo flew to a tree and landed. The Great Ancestor spoke from it once more, 'THERE IS A COST FOR THE SUN AND FOR TONAH LEAH, FOREVER ONWARDS THE BLACK COCKATOO WILL BE KNOWN AS MENNUGGANA AND WILL BE THE MESSENGER OF BAD NEWS.'"

"Is that true Dad?" said Nicki, doubtfully.

"I reckon so, my mother and father always said that when a black cockatoo was about there was bad news in the air. And you just look at the yellow tail feathers on a black cockatoo next time yuh see one," said Ben confidently.

"What about the fire spirit dear?" asked Marge.

"Yes," said Ben, "the next day a fire was burning near the Pydairrerme camp, just like our camp fire, anyway the people made small torches of the

fire to carry around with them." He paused, and then, "The people would sometimes lose their fire, but Tonah Leah would send lightning from the skies and make more fire. Later, the people learnt to make fire, but because it was easy to carry they did that more often than make it."

Just then a big streak of lightning lit up the night, it was way out to sea though. "I wonder why Tonah Leah tries to make fire at sea, Dad?" says Nicki with some mischief in her voice.

Ben is not fazed, "Tonah Leah is the fire spirit and must be able to make fire when it's needed, that's why that spirit practises out to sea."

Marge's voice comes back quickly, "Yes, well if you don't practise pretty often right here this camp fire is gonna need Tonah Leah to get it goin' again."

Ben got up without a word and went to get more wood from the pile near the tent. He looked up at another flash of lightning and smiled, he was thinking that perhaps Kakannawayreetya was unhappy at being the fire spirit, or it might be just a way of letting us know he's still with us.

Right
The hazards faced by Tasmania's first settlers were very different from those confronting most mainland tribes. Good water, for example, was available almost everywhere. Ice-age cold on the other hand was, for thousands of years, a very serious problem.

Following pages
Ballroom Forest, Cradle Mountain, Lake Saint Clair National Park.

WESTERN AUSTRALIA

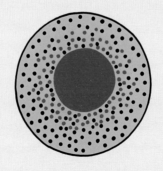

The carpets of flowers that follow good rains, even in the most arid regions, are a continual reminder of the vast genetic reservoir that lies dormant in all desert soils. Among the commonest flowers of the Great Victoria Desert are purple mulla mullas and these bright yellow podolepis.

*B*ibulmum is the name of a large community of Aboriginal people who once, with other communities, occupied the fertile southwestern corner of Western Australia. With the arrival of the Europeans the once-independent communities came together into a nation now known as The Nyoongah. Mudrooroo Nyoongah was born at Narogin in the Nyoongah nation and his stories reflect the tradition of storytelling of his people.

"A Snake Story for Kids" is about the Waugyal being which inhabits the rivers of the southwest and which looks after Nyoongahs when they cross flowing water. "The Source of the Djangan" is a composite story made up from various versions he has heard about the Nyoongah's greatest hero, Djangan, and how he met his death.

Different peoples, the Wongyr from the goldfields and others from the Kimberley enter the country of the Nyoongahs and good relations exist between them. The late Gloria Brennan was a vital woman of the Wongyr and a good friend of Mudrooroo's. She passed on "My Son's Dreaming Story" as a connection between his son and her country. It is his son's story and must be seen as a charter of rights, an umbilical cord attaching him to the land.

Despite appearances, all environments are but passing shows. In a curious paradox the most abundant evidence that Australia was once encased in ice now lies crumbling in the heat of its western deserts. The Poole Range southeast of the Kimberleys appears to be largely composed of glacially derived sediments that were dumped at the edge of a receding ice-sheet nearly 300 million years ago.

The creation story of ancestral beings roaming across the
western deserts to central Australia, lifting hills out of the
flat plains as they went, has a thread of geological fact to
it. The western half of the continent appears to have been
squeezed between Antarctica and some Asian landmasses
about 600 million years ago. It crumpled across the
middle to form an unbroken chain of mountains almost
2,000 kilometres long. Most of that has since worn away
however, and except from some remnants at its eastern
end, such as the Petermann Ranges, the rest now lies
submerged beneath the sands of the western desert.

Following page
This curious bed of sandstone, weathering like cracked
elephant hide, originated as a massive bed of sediment
that had been washed from beneath a melting ice-sheet
about 280 million years ago.

MY SON'S DREAMING STORY

We go back a long way in this country. A long, long way back, even before the beginning of people, animals and plants. That's how far back I'm talking about. Then there was only Mummy Sun. She kept on crossing and recrossing the bare flat earth. It made her feel very sad and lonely. There were no wattle trees, no kangaroos, no snakes, no people. It was so bare that there wasn't even a mozzie or a fly. Everywhere nothing, and this made the earth feel sad too. The sadness rose up and met the sadness of Mummy Sun drifting down. Both sisters were sad, so very sad that they caused the first rain drops to fall. The rain fell, entered the ground and turned into seeds.

Now here's a difficult part. It needs thinking about. Those seeds came up, but were not the plants we have around us today. They were the mummies and daddies of the plants, the animals and people. These were our first parents. The mummies and daddies of everything. We belong to one huge family and have to take care of all our relations.

Now time began and eventually people came. Your story is about two men. Two brothers, or as we say in the language: *jingani* to each other. Kurukadi was the oldest and he looked after his younger brother, Mumba. They lived in the Kimberleys, right above our Nyoongah country. They were very good workers. They loved to work and kept on working and working. And why did they work? They thought the ground was too flat and smooth. No good for plants and animals and people. Definitely no good for kids. So they got to work to change it. They dug out rivers and lakes, heaped up

mountains and planted trees in the gorges. Kurukadi and Mumba travelled all over their country fixing things. They were such good workers that the day came when they had nothing left to do.

"What's next?" asked Kurukadi. "Dunno," replied Mumba. And so they lay under the shade of the very first tree they had grown and thought and thought. They needed work, for idle hands…but that's another story. What to do? Thinking tired them out more than work. At last Kurukadi had an idea. He leapt to his feet and striking a pose with one hand outstretched (guess you thought I was going to say that he stood on one leg, but you only find that in the picture books), he said: "That country next to ours. It could do with a bit of a fixing."

Mumba got up and also assumed a pose. He shaded his eyes with a hand as he gazed into the distance while replying: "It does need a bit of looking after."

At once, they started walking towards the southeast. As they went they built up hills and excavated wells. The way they travelled can still be seen today. There is a line of wells leading from the Kimberley in a southeasterly direction into the desert.

Now we get to our hero, Kalu. He was born in a desert place he named Pirakata. But unlike Kurukadi and Mumba, he wasn't interested in working. So, after digging a nice well for water and planting a few flowers around to make the place attractive, he just took it easy.

Now don't get the idea that Kalu was lazy. A lot of you might jump to this conclusion, but the truth is that Kalu had a great plan in his head. The plan was so big that often his head throbbed as if it was going to fly off into space. You know what his problem was? The feeling of blackness. That's right, the blackness of the night. It got to him so much that he became

Great Victoria Desert.

afraid of the dark. So afraid of the dark, that he had to call out for his Mummy, but she was nowhere in sight. He had to wait until morning time, when Mummy Sun sailed overhead with her great golden face beaming love down at him. It was then that he felt so much better and could try and forget the scary darkness. But it hung in his mind and no matter how brightly Mummy Sun shone, it still remained. It was then that he got this tremendous idea. He wanted to put a huge light in the sky so that the night would not be scary any more.

But how to, how to? He thought and thought, while on the horizon towards the northwest marvellous things were happening. As the two brothers came closer and closer, they built up the Warburton Ranges. Hills grew all around Kalu, but still he dreamt on, growing weak and pale from too much thought.

Finally, the two brothers reached Kalu. They found him stretched out beside his well doing what he did best, thinking. They were upset by the sight of him. Kalu was very pale and very fat. His cheeks bulged and his double chin rested on a belly as round as a balloon. Worst of all, because he never did any exercise, his legs and arms had grown into four thin sticks. He was a sorry sight indeed; but he still cherished his great plan.

The two brothers shook their heads. Kalu ignored them. They coughed to get his attention. Kalu still ignored them. They stamped on the ground. Kalu stirred. At last, they shouted. Kalu came out of the darkness of his thoughts. He greeted the brothers courteously and invited them to camp beside his well.

When they had settled in, Kalu listened as they told him about their work. They had built so many wonderful things. It was only then that he noticed the mountains all about him. He looked around at his own creation.

A small well, a few hollows in the ground for shelter from the wind, a small pile of boulders covered with tiny yellow flowers which he still found soothing to look at when the thoughts of darkness frightened him too much.

It was then that he began telling the brothers about his plan to put a huge light in the sky. He waited for them to laugh. He expected them to laugh, but they didn't even smile. He was an Iparuka man like themselves* and entitled to the same respect that they expected from others. When Kalu stopped talking, Kurukadi replied modestly: "Well, you know, we're pretty good at doing things…" and Mumba agreed, "Yes, we are."

But how to put the huge light in the sky? They thought and thought. All at once, the two brothers knew how it was to be done. Kalu too knew. It frightened him. He didn't want to be big and grown-up and able to do things.

"You know, we make a boomerang like this," Kurukadi began. "A large one shaped like this," agreed Mumba, sketching a sickle shape on the ground.

"But, but you know, maybe…" hesitated Kalu. "And after we make it…" started Kurukadi, "We place Kalu on it and fling it high into the sky," finished off Mumba.

"Hurray," said Kalu, excited by seeing his dream at last becoming real. Then he thought a bit and asked: "But how will this help to light the night and stop us from being scared?"

"Look, have you ever seen yourself?" asked Kurukadi. He scooped out a few handfuls of earth and absent-mindedly sprinkled them about. Spinifex grass sprang up. In the hollow, a spring of water gushed. It settled into a smooth and shining surface. "Take a look," he invited Kalu. "Who is that, so filled with light?"

*Of the same clan.

One of the most endearing features of desert life is its
overwhelming response to good rains. By necessity most
of its plants and animals are opportunists, bursting into a
feverish cycle of reproduction as soon as conditions
become favourable rather than waiting for a particular
seasonal trigger.

Previous page

It is easy to see, especially at sunset, why the people of the
western deserts attributed special significance to the few low hills that
break the level horizons of the sandplains. This rock shelter near
the Warburton Ranges looks out over a sea of sand that stretches
almost unbroken to the Pilbara on the west coast.

Generation after generation of ice-age hunters must have
sat in this cave near the southeastern edge of the
Kimberleys ritualistically sharpening their stone weapons
on the rock wall. Curiously, the rock itself is a relic of a
previous ice age. It is formed from rock debris, silt, gravel
and boulders, that fell from the sole of a glacier where it
met the sea some 280-300 million years ago.

Previous pages
When the monsoon strays into Australia's arid heartland it
triggers a chain-reaction of enormous proportions. With
virtually no drainage system to carry the water away, it
produces an explosion of new life over a vast area,
effectively recharging the desert's genetic batteries
with enough new material to keep its biological engines
ticking over for years to come.

"So cool and glistening," added Mumba, ambling over to look. "You're the one for this job," they both declared.

"I am the one for this job," smiled Kalu, entranced by his image in the water. Reluctantly, he pulled his face away as he thought again. "But, but, won't it be awful lonely up there? I'll miss you two. We're Iparuka men and have to stick together."

Kurukadi glanced at his brother Mumba. Not only were they Iparuka men, but they were fond of the little fellow. "Well," began Kurukadi. "Well?" queried Mumba.

"You know," continued Kurukadi, "after we finish our work here, we start on the sky world. There's bound to be lots to do up there. We'll set up a camp close by and you can drop in when you feel like it."

"And on weekends," added Mumba, "we'll get together and have a barbie."

Kalu, with the habit of thought, had to pick at everything. "But how will the light shine when I go to visit you?"

"Just you leave that to us. We're good at doing things."

Kalu had neglected to make any trees at Pirakata, but the two brothers remedied this by planting them at Djilanda, a nearby place where they had set up their workshop.

The trees grew quickly and in a day or two they were ready. Kurukadi selected the thickest mulga tree. It was a beauty and far bigger and taller than the mulga trees you see today. Mumba marked out the shape of a crescent boomerang on it. Then the two brothers reached down into the earth and drew out a clear stone, as hard and as sharp as diamond. Quickly, they sliced their way through the hard wood. When it was finished Mumba went to get Kalu while Kurukadi returned the stones to the earth. He then

took out a yellow ochre which Kalu had once deposited there. This he smeared all over the boomerang. Now it shone like silver.

Although it was a short distance away, Kalu didn't like walking to Djilanda. Mumba urged him on, but all that he could manage was a slow waddle. Then in the distance the boomerang gleamed. It stirred him into a waddling run. By the time he reached the workshop he was exhausted.

Kurukadi led him to the boomerang. Weakly, he slumped on to it. It felt soft and even cuddly. Contentedly, he sank back and wasn't even amazed when Kurukadi began growing into a giant. In fact, he was so tired that he dozed off and missed all the action. The giant Kurukadi held the crescent boomerang containing the sleeping Kalu by the tip, then with a gentle flip sent it whirling up and up into the sky. Suddenly it was lost to sight. The brothers stared up. Kalu must be all right; he must be; for he was an Iparuka man and it would be bad if they let harm come to him.

Anxiously, they waited for Mummy Sun to go to sleep. Not too soon for them, she sank below the horizon. Then, all at once, for the very first time appeared in the sky the moon. Kalu floated pale and glistening safely tucked up in his bed.

In an age-old ritual, the creation spirit of Kalu climbs between the crumbling domes of Bungle Bungle to chase the darkness from the desert skies.

Right
Despite appearances Australia does
indeed have its vast herds of grazing
animals. But unlike Africa they are
all underground. In the deserts
especially, the vegetarian at the
base of the predatory food-chain
is the humble termite. Secure
in their underground redoubts
they regularly survive such
environmental assaults as fire,
drought and flood with equal
impunity, lending a firm base to the
most fragile ecologies.

Following pages
Showing more similarity to cactus
than to its real relatives, one curious
member of the hibiscus family, the
dunna dunna, displays spectacular
adaptation to life on the hot, dry
claypans at the western edge of the
Gibson Desert. To combat water loss
through its foliage it has reduced its
leaves until they encase the stems
in a sleeve of tiny scales. Australia's
original settlers achieved a similar
order of adaptation in a fraction
of the time merely by modifying
their behaviour.

166

A SNAKE STORY FOR THE KIDS

This is a story about our big snake. European people don't like snakes. They tell us that they are bad and good-for-nothing; but to us Nyoongah people, the ancestor of all the snakes, the Waugyal, made his home in our land and he became special to us. He settled down here after he had made all the world. And why did he decide to live here? I guess he found our country beautiful and restful, or he just grew tired as he went along making the Swan River. If you look at how lazy and slow this river is, you can see just how weary he was by this time.

Now, just before I get into this story, I'd better tell you a bit more about our Waugyal. After he had crawled all the way up into the Darling Ranges, he returned and went to sleep in a deep part of the Swan River. He's still there; but these days he's restless. There is too much noise from speed boats and water skiers and things like that. Sometimes, the noise is so much that he wakes up. Then he becomes upset and angry. At times he becomes so upset that he causes all the fish to leave the river; other times he capsizes the noisiest of the boats.

Well, a couple of years ago, one of our Nyoongah lads decided that he wanted to go sailing on the river. Now, if you want to go sailing, the first thing you need is a boat, and our boy didn't have one. In fact none of the Nyoongahs had a boat. Still, this didn't put him off, and so he went to talk to one of the grandfathers. They were as old as the hills and knew just about everything. This one did know how to make a canoe. He told the boy that in the old days, the Nyoongahs had made canoes from a big sheet of bark.

They had shaped this over a fire, then joined the ends together with clay, or gum. Without waiting to hear anything more, the lad raced away. He knew he could make a canoe.

But first of all, he had to find a big enough piece of bark. This stumped him. He was *only* nine — at least his mummy always told him so when he wanted to go off and adventure, though nine became a *big* nine when he was to behave himself. But for all the figuring of his mother, he still found himself too small to hack off a sheet of bark from a standing tree. Then he remembered the sawmill nearby. He raced off and lo and behold he found a curved sheet of bark just off a log. Staggering under its length, he managed to get it to the banks of the river. He lit a small fire and placed the sheet on it. Instantly, it caught alight. He splashed water over the flames, but it was ruined. There was a big hole right through the middle.

He was about to give up the idea of ever sailing on the Swan when he saw a sheet of galvanised iron lying on the ground nearby. It was just the right size and stronger than bark. After a good deal of bashing with a piece of steel, he managed to bend the iron into a shape near that of a canoe. There still remained the problem of how to join the ends together. Also there were rows of nail holes across the tin and these had to be plugged.

The grandfather had told him that in the old days clay or gum had been used. He decided to use a piece of wood nailed between the joins. This looked professional, but when he dragged it to the water, he had to save his craft from quickly sinking. He dragged the canoe out of the water and pondered on the problem. Maybe he should use clay, or gum. But there wasn't any around. He felt the dampness of the bank beneath his pants and had the answer. He would use mud.

The side-necked turtle, now one of the world's rarest
creatures, was once common in the many swamps and
lakes that backed on to the coastal dune system near
Perth, the State's fast-growing capital. The urban sprawl
that accompanied its growth has restricted these turtles
to two small swamps at the city's northern limits, and
reduced their numbers in the wild to less than 30.

Previous page
The Swan River used to wind across the sandy coastal
plain to the sea through a mixture of woodland and scrub
that was dotted with small lakes and marshes. Wildlife
was abundant and food was plentiful for its original
custodians. It had remained this way for them despite a
tenancy that had spanned a minimum of 40,000 years,
and perhaps almost three times that period.

Just the thing, at least that's what he thought. He enjoyed plastering it over the joins and the nail holes. By the time he had finished and had a rest, the hot sun had dried the mud as hard as stone and as strong as rock. He pushed the canoe into the river and not a drop of water entered. It took a bit of a balancing act to get into the canoe, but he managed it. He had already placed in the canoe two flat pieces of wood for paddles. Wobbling dangerously, he moved along the shore. Not a drop of water came into the canoe and he quickly mastered the art of paddling it smoothly along. Confidently, he headed out into the middle of the river. It was the furthest he had ever been from shore. Why, he could cross over right now, if he wanted to.

It was just then that he felt a wetness creeping along his bottom. He looked down. Water was pouring through where the mud had been. Frantically, he paddled, but the water rushed in and the canoe settled lower and lower. He was faced with a watery grave. What could he do? His young life began flashing through his mind, just as he had heard from his elders. Now he knew that his end was nigh and he was scared. He began praying, used up his Christian gods and saints, and decided to ask the Waugyal for help. After all, he was a Nyoongah boy and when a Nyoongah is in trouble he goes to his own kin and culture.

That very day, Waugyal had been on an outing. He too had relatives and sometimes he went down to the sea to visit. Now, after a good yarn, he was on his way back upstream. He yawned as he approached his sleeping hole. A shadow wobbled over it. Puzzled, he thrust his head above the water and saw the sinking canoe. He also saw the desperate Nyoongah boy and heard the prayer. Quick as a flash, he ducked down and came up beneath the canoe. It rested on his broad back.

The boy felt his canoe beginning to move towards the shore. He looked down and saw the long dark body of Waugyal just beneath the water. As he was a Nyoongah, he wasn't scared. He knew that Waugyal was part of his Dreaming and would never hurt him. So he just sat there and enjoyed the ride back to shore. When Waugyal left the canoe in shallow water, he said "Thank you, Mr Waugyal." He waded ashore and raced off to his family, for to tell the truth, he was a little shaky after his adventure and hungry too.

Clutching a thick piece of bread and jam, between mouthfuls he told his family what had happened. Immediately, his father forbade him to go out in that canoe ever again. Then to make him happy, added that he knew all about making canoes out of sheets of galvanised iron and would make him a better one that weekend. "Who knows, I might even go for a ride in it myself and see Waugyal," he chuckled, hitting at his paunch which would never ever fit into a canoe.

Ilyarrie gum, Perth.

The city of Perth, Western Australia's
fast-growing capital, rises into the
glow of a stormy sunset.

SOURCE OF THE DJANGAN

You know one time, not so long ago, this place all pines. Pines as far as your eye can see. Just pine trees. Lots of cockies too. Black cockies, swarms of them. Good eating, dark flesh — but, you know, tasty! Anyway, here, they planted pines all over, all over the place. Cut down the gum trees to do it. Tuarts, they were. Just over there and there, you can see the stumps. Big ones, aren't they? You should have seen the trees. Should have; but even those pines are all gone now and this university, this Murdoch University has taken over the place. That's where we are now, at Murdoch University. It's a nice place; not too big, and those stumps are part of it. They must date from Djangan's time. Well, Djangan? You never heard of him. He was one of our big fellows, big strong man.

All this was his country, long before the *watjelas** came. Djangan's country! Strong fellow that one. Powerful; but, you know, he had one weakness. Don't know where he got it, or why he got it, but he had it. Maybe part of his dreaming, maybe not — still, it belonged to him. Yeah, it did. Now, this country all around here, we used to call it Beeliar. Big rich country: lots of duck, swan, kangaroo, bush carrots and all that plant food. No cockies then, they came with the pine trees; no rabbits then, they came with the *djangaras,** you know, *watjelas.* All this country belonged to Djangan and his family. What you call tribe — for all of us were related in those days. Just one big happy family. His father was Midgigoroo, his mother — just can't recall her name, but her brother was Nyinyinnee. You know what they did to him, the *watjelas?* They shot him down just like a kangaroo. They trapped

*European.

177

him next to the water at Fremantle. He was sitting down, resting, then a *watjela* crept near and bang. He shot him just like that. They killed him for his head. They hacked it off. With a tommyhawk. One, two, three blows and it was off his neck. Then, then they smoked it, just like you smoke a ham. They sent it off to England to add to the collection they had there. It was part of their magic, part of their empire, collecting skulls. We were frightened of them. Head hunters. Have it off, as soon as look at you. They were real *djaŋgaras.* That was what we called them in those days, *djaŋgara,* ghosts.

Anyway, this was Djangan's country. All around here and he died in his country. They killed him just a way along the road towards the causeway. Just down from it, near where they have that statue now. It was there, just after Djangan had crossed the water, not once, but twice. That was his undoing. If he had not crossed that water, he probably would still be alive. He had power that one. Real *maban.* No one could get the better of him!

Well, what happened, why did he cross that water? No fault of his. He knew better. No fault of his. The *djaŋgara* took him. They found him at the river. He had gone there to fish. Get some mullet, maybe some mud crabs. Then this boat came along. You know what we used to call a white man's boat. We called it *wuŋdab-buri,* because it was shaped like a shield. Well, that boat came crawling along on the water. In it were those *djaŋgaras* who dressed in red — soldiers! Well, they rowed along to where Djangan and his uncle, Doumera, and his wife's brother, Nyinyinnee were fishing. They had a pile of fish beside them and I guess that the soldiers were jealous. So they rowed right up and grabbed the fish and the three men. Put them in the boat and went off. Guess, they had the fish for supper that night; but the three Nyoongahs — they took them across the water. Flowing water! Djangan felt his strength ebbing out of him.

Kangaroo Paw, Perth.

A long time they were on water. A long long time. The *djangara* were taking the three Nyoongahs to their secret place. Their prison place surrounded by water, in the middle of water, cut off by water. Up and down the water moved. Djangan chucked out his power. He became limp and pale like a ghost.

At last, they reached the *djangaras'* secret place. A big flat rock surrounded by water. We called it Ngooloormayup*. In the Dreaming the remains of Binnar had flashed to the earth; burnt the earth down to rock, and left it strewn with pebbles. Here Djangan and his two uncles were flung. Here they were kept, and on the third day it seemed that Binnar flashed down again. Before them appeared a *djangara* with three bags. One bag held white flour, the second held whiteman's clothing, the third held his magic. The *djangara* came up to where Djangan, Doumera and Nyinyinnee were lying, weak and hungry. So weak that their chests barely trembled. Then Binnar fumbled in his bag of magic and pulled out a shining stone, a *madjit-til* and placed it to the lips of the three men. It was as if a fire flowed down their throats. A fire without flame. It gave strength, but not power to Djangan and his two uncles. They got to their feet. Now Binnar clothed the three in whitemen's clothing, and set them to work. They scraped the island and gathered up the pebbles. These were tipped into the sea at one end of the rock. At the southern end where across the way rests Meeandip* — a forbidden place to them.

Now, Djangan began swallowing some of the pebbles. Power flowed from them into his kidneys. One day, filled with strength, he defied Binnar.

*Garden Island.

*Rottnest Island.

"I won't scrape this island for you any longer," he declared. Doumera and Nyinyinnee shouted: "We won't work for you either."

Binnar smiled and pointed at the water falling and rising; at the white-man's boat rising and falling. But Djangan had the power in him. He knew he could cross that water. He called out to Doumera and Nyinyinnee to bring long sticks. They got on to the shield. He untied the boat. They poled it out to deep water. They floated to the mouth of the Swan River. The tide was just right. It carried them up and along. At last, they drifted to the shore near where they now have that statue. They were glad to leave the water, but it had taken all their power and strength. They staggered a little way from the bank, then collapsed, fell down and into a deep sleep under a sheltering tree.

They were exhausted, especially Djangan. The waters had mastered his power. It had forced the pebbles from his stomach. Now, defenceless he lay sleeping; and as he lay, two young *djangara* crept to him. One, named John, clutched a tommyhawk; the other, called Rich, dangled a noose. He flung it over Djangan's neck and jerked it tight. Djangan struggled awake. His hands tugged at the noose, but they had no strength. Then John raised his hatchet and brought it down on Djangan's neck. The life blood streamed forth. It flowed across the ground, into a hollow at the base of the tree, then down to the river. It sank beneath the water and stained the mud red. You can still see that red mud near the causeway. And the tree, well scratch through the bark of that tree and it bleeds the blood of Djangan.

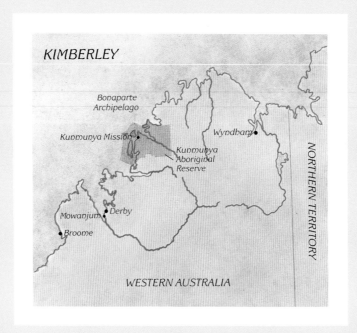

KIMBERLEY

Tidal Bay off Talbot Bay,
McLarty Range.

*T*he three Aboriginal clans who speak the languages Worora, Ngarinyin and Wun-
ambal traditionally shared the Prince Regent River and Mitchell Plateau portion
of the Kimberley. During the 1950s, as a matter of survival, many of the descendants
of the three groups moved south and settled together at Mowanjum, close to Derby,
where they inevitably led a more European way of life.

Daisy Utemorrah is strongly connected with each of the three language groups
and is a member of the Mowanjum community. She was born at Kunmunya Mission
in 1922, and writes, "I grew up and stayed with my parents. We lived in a humpy hut.
In those days the mission didn't have many houses. And so I loved living in the hut. I
went out to the bush with my parents. We camped out for three or four days.

"I loved the bush very much. I was taught by my parents and grandparents the
bush life. I visited the caves and they told me the Dreamtime stories which I kept all
the time."

The swelling outstation movement of recent years has meant that many of
those at Mowanjum, including Daisy, have been able to return at last to their own
country for extended periods. There they live on bush food, sleep under tents, care
for the sacred caves and rock art, and teach stories and rules to the children in the
traditional style.

Daisy is well regarded as a storyteller and writer. The following story first
appeared in *Visions of Mowanjum*, published by Rigby. The poems are from Daisy's
collection *Do Not Go Around the Edges*, recently released by Magabala Books.

The first poem's subtitle "Bunju Bunju" is the name of a nasty old wizard who
lures people away. "Galanji" is the island on which Daisy's grandparents were born.

HOW THE PEOPLE WERE ALL DROWNED

A long, long time ago in the Dreaming, there lived a tribe called the Dillangari people. They were like most other tribes, except that their dogs were as big as calves.

One day the tribesmen were talking about the dogs. "Why can't dogs talk?" asked one man. Someone explained that Wandjina had told the dog he was always to bark, and never to talk like a human. If by any chance he did speak Wandjina would drown all the people.

So parents were very careful to tell their children never to tease a dog.

One day the people decided to go to another part of their country. They found a place where there was a river and plenty of food — yams, roots, berries and wild honey. The men said to their wives, "We are going hunting for kangaroo; see that the children stay close to you and don't let them tease the dogs. We don't want to be drowned, and that's what will happen if the dogs start talking like us."

"All right," replied the women, "we will see to the children."

The men went off and the women gathered the children together and warned them, "Children, you must listen very carefully and do what we tell you. First of all, you must not hit any special bird which belongs to Wandjina, such as Tumbi, the Owl. If you do, the Wandjina will send rain and storms and we all will be drowned. And the second thing is that you must not tease the dogs. Don't try to make them talk like us because Wandjina has told the dogs that they are only allowed to bark."

The strange, mouthless, spirit figures known as Wandjinas seem to have exerted a powerful influence throughout the Kimberley region. Unique to the area and credited with considerable power they were a common subject for the artists of old, and haunting images of them still stare from the shadows of innumerable Kimberley rock shelters.

Previous pages
The world's most spectacular tide race lies deep in Worora country at the eastern end of Talbot Bay. For almost 24 hours of each day the sea thunders in and out of two former river gorges, flooding and draining the valleys beyond. Powered by a tidal fluctuation that sometimes exceeds nine metres, and constrained by the width of the two narrow gorges, the water here is still and silent for no more than about two minutes at each tide change.

186

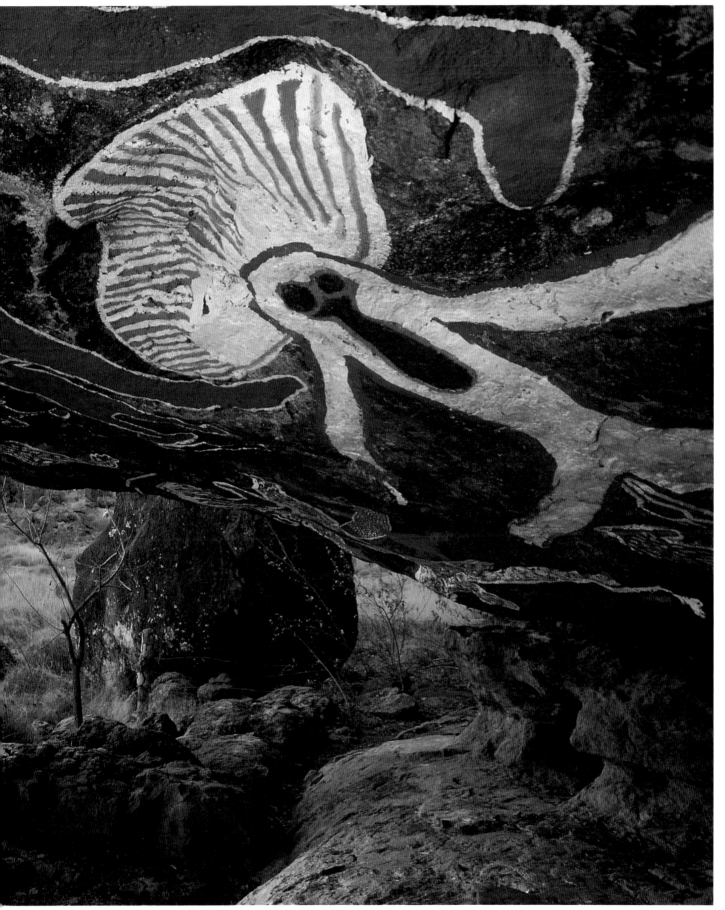

D. PARER AND E. PARER-COOK, AUSCAPE INTERNATIONAL

The dingo appears to have arrived in Australia somewhere around 4,000 years ago, brought here no doubt as hunting dogs and family pets by people moving down the Indonesian island chain from Asia. The dingo's hunting prowess was widely respected and it soon became embedded in the art and oral culture of most tribes. This painting decorates the walls of a rock shelter known as Dog Cave in the Napier Range in the southeastern Kimberley.

The children asked why they couldn't play with the dogs, and the women answered, "If you do, and a dog answers you, we will all be swallowed up by water. No one will survive. The Wandjina will cause the water to rise and drown us all."

So the children agreed to leave the dogs alone.

Some of the women went off to look for berries and wild honey and yams. The remaining women were told to keep an eye on the children, but instead of doing this, they went down to the river to gather waterlily roots.

A group of children started to play with the dogs, calling and yelling to them. The women were so busy with the waterlily roots that they didn't hear the children, who continued to tease the dogs. Suddenly one of the dogs answered back, speaking like a human.

As soon as that happened, Wandjina caused the whole tribe to disappear under the ground and under the water. Only the Wandjina themselves were left.

As evening drew on, another Wandjina was walking towards that place. He looked around for the people but couldn't hear a sound. He was very sorry and decided to go to the caves where the Spirit Dog lived.

He walked very slowly and when he came close to the cave he called out. "Ngunaguri, are you there?"

"Yes," replied Ngunaguri, the Spirit Dog, "what is it you want to see me about?" The Wandjina replied "I am looking for the people. Where are they? What have you done with them?"

"Well," said Ngunaguri, "I am very sorry to tell you that they are all drowned because the children were disobedient. They were teasing the dogs and making them talk like humans. I had warned them many times, but

Tidal waterfall, Talbot Bay.

they didn't believe me and kept on. So I caused them all to be swallowed up, and that's the end of them."

"Oh no!" cried the Wandjina angrily. "The people will come back again in the Dreamtime. Others living on this land will dream them up and bring them back to life and they will be their parents. I will put a curse over you so that these people will be your master once and for all. You will never be allowed to talk to anyone. You will only be able to bark." And before the Spirit Dog could do anything about it, the Wandjina had put this curse on him.

But the Wandjina was still very sad without the people and he kept calling to them until at last he heard a voice: "What do you want us to do?"

"Well," said the Wandjina, "in your Dreamtime, bring other people to you and you can be mothers and fathers to them. You will be the Dillangari, to represent the dog."

And it is remembered until this day how the dog spoke and the people were banished underground. That's why Aborigines all over the Kimberley still stop their children from teasing the dogs.

Midwinter in the Kimberleys has many attractive features, not least of which are flowers such as these on a eucalypt known as the woollybutt. It was traditionally a time of ease for the nomadic peoples of the northwest coast, a time when the rock pools were still full and there was food aplenty.

Kapok bush, King Leopold Range.

Right

As one of Australia's ancient continental cornerstones the Kimberley region has an astonishingly long and varied geological record. It has in turn been flooded with molten lava, entombed by sheets of ice, invaded by seas, clothed in lush rainforest, and now scorched almost to desert. Among its more bizarre souvenirs of these events are the remnants of a huge barrier reef that once looped around three sides of it. The multitude of caves carved into its limestone provided local clans with excellent shelter and a broad canvas for their art.

GALANJI

Far far away far far away

is my Island home

called Galanji

Far far away!

Far far away

is my Island home!

Aw-aw-aw.

The Worora people of the Kimberley coast are traditional custodians of one of the most dramatically dissected shorelines in the world. It is a region of innumerable islands, secluded bays, precipitous headlands, mangrove-lined estuaries and vast mudflats. Its true character, that of an old, drowned coastline, comes graphically alive when it is seen from the air. This view looks north across Talbot Bay to the islands of the Buccaneer Archipelago.

Previous pages
Tidal bays, McLarty Range.

Gantheaume Point, Broome.

Right
Silt-loaded eddies in the daily ebb and flow of the gigantic
tides that wash the Kimberley's shores have added their
own peculiar ornamentation to an already spectacular
coastline. This frond-like promontory extends into a
northwestern arm of Talbot Bay, in Worora country north
of Derby. The difficulties of moving about such a dissected
coast ensured that the Worora were a robust, vigorous
people skilled in the arts of navigation.

DO NOT GO AROUND THE EDGES (BUNJU BUNJU)

Do not go around the edges

or else you'll fall.

No good that place

or else you slip.

The scour of the huge tides that characterise the coast of northwestern Australia ensure that they are always loaded with silt. In more sheltered backwaters this silt has re-settled to form broad tidal mudflats. Here only mangroves flourish, delineating rivers and tidal drainage channels with a rich, green fringe. These big intertidal zones provided a valuable addition to the food-gathering grounds of the coastal clans and much variety in the daily diet.

Boab trees are endemic to the Kimberley region and hold a special significance for its people. They believed that the boab represented a special creation by the Wandjina spirits of the Dreamtime. Every part of it is useful. An old tree might provide them with an emergency water supply from reservoirs hidden in its trunk; with fibre for rope, and a medicine, from its crushed bark; with a glue from its pollen; and with a food source in the pith of its big seed pods.

FURTHER READING

Burnam Burnam, *Aboriginal Australia*. Angus and Robertson, 1988.

Davis, Jack, and Bob Hodge, *Aboriginal Writing Today*. Aboriginal Studies Press, 1985.

Davis, Jack, Stephen Muecke, Mudrooroo Narogin, Adam Shoemaker (editors), *Paperbark: A Collection of Black Australian Writing*. University of Queensland Press, 1990.

Everett, Jim, and Karen Brown, *The Spirit of Kuti Kina*. Eumarrah Publications, 1990.

Isaacs, Jennifer, *Australian Aboriginal Paintings*, Weldon, 1989.

Mountford, Charles P., *The Dreamtime*. Art Australia, 1965.

Narogin, Mudrooroo, *Doin Wildcat*, Hyland House, 1988.
    Writing from the Fringe. Hyland House, 1990.

Neidjie, Bill, *Australia's Kakadu Man Bill Neidjie*. Resource Managers, 1986.
    Story About Feeling. Magabala Books, 1989.

Noonuccal, Oodgeroo, *see* Walker, Kath.

Noonuccal, Oodgeroo, and Kabul Oodgeroo Noonuccal, *The Rainbow Serpent*. Australian Government Publishing Service, 1988.

Premont, Roslyn, and Mark Lennard, *Tjukurrpa: Desert Paintings of Central Australia*. Centre for Aboriginal Artists, 1988.

Robinson, Roland (collector), *The Nearest White Man Gets: Aboriginal Narratives and Poems of New South Wales*. Hale and Iremonger, 1989.

Roe, Paddy, and Stephen Muecke, *Gularabulu: Stories from the West Kimberleys*. Fremantle Arts Centre Press, 1983.

Roth, H. Ling, *The Aborigines of Tasmania*. F. King and Sons, 1899.

Ryan, Lyndall, *The Aboriginal Tasmanians*. University of Queensland Press, 1981.

Steele, John G., *Aboriginal Pathways: Southeast Queensland and the Richmond River*. University of Queensland Press, 1987.

Tilbrook, Lois, *Nyungar Tradition: Glimpses of Aborigines of South-Western Australia 1829-1914*. University of Western Australia Press, 1983.

Tunbridge, Dorothy, *Flinders Ranges Dreaming*. Aboriginal Studies Press, 1988.

Utemorrah, Daisy, *Do Not Go Around the Edges*. Magabala Books, 1990.

Visions of Mowanjum: Aboriginal Writings from the Kimberley. Rigby, 1980.

Walker, Kath (Oodgeroo Noonuccal)
    — *We Are Going*. Jacaranda Wiley, 1964.
    — *The Dawn Is At Hand*. Jacaranda Wiley, 1966.
    — *Stradbroke Dreamtime*. Angus and Robertson, 1970.
    — *Father Sky and Mother Earth*. Jacaranda Wiley, 1981.
    — *My People*. Jacaranda Wiley, 1981, revised 1990.
    — *Kath Walker in China*. Jacaranda Wiley, 1990.

West, Ida, *Pride Against Prejudice: Reminiscences of a Tasmanian Aborigine*. Australian Institute of Aboriginal Studies, 1984.

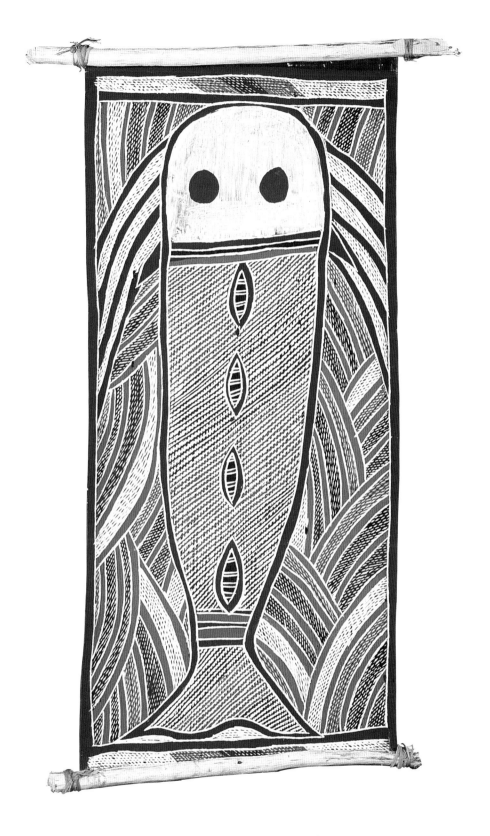

Whale. Milminyina, Eastern Arnhem
Land, late 1980s.